EVOLUTION'S
A BITCH

Catfighting in Cool Britannia

Tirny Francis

Van Waterson Publications

ISBN13: 978-1-9168970-1-4

Cover design by: Buzbooks.com

Printed in the United Kingdom

To all the catfighters out there.
You are life itself.

CONTENTS

CHAPTER 1
BAPTISM OF FIRE

I can't remember how or where we both agreed to see if we could fix her up a match. There was a website called Excite (or maybe it was Yahoo!) which had 'interest groups' and we were able to identify a few potential opponents. Some of the profiles were obviously guys pretending to be girls, or were soon rumbled to be, but we did manage to locate a few genuine 'possibles.'

It was the beginning of 1997 and I had recently discovered 'Barb's page' on the Internet. At the time it was THE place for female-wrestling afficionados of both sexes. Not 'professional wrestling,' but real wrestling between real women. I could hardly believe that such a scene existed. The site identified a list of vendors who sold videos catering to this unusual taste, but also made clear that this was an activity that real women participated in for fun. While not exactly widespread, it was not a complete rarity either.

Barb's site opened up an Aladdin's cave of video-based excitement, and before long I was using the Internet to purchase videocassettes from all over the world which featured young women fighting each other. When international packages began arriving at my house bearing postmarks from Chicago or Vienna, my heartbeat rose, and I would look forward to spending entire evenings devoted to watching the matches. I had never found most pornography to be particularly stimulating, but there was something particularly arousing about the passion which the amateur competitors on video brought to their contests.

The matches were not high-school-style amateur wrestling, where the objective would have been to achieve pins against an opponent, but submission wrestling, where the aim was to extract submissions through the use of painful wrestling holds. Young women, usually between the ages of 18 and 30, would participate in non-scripted bouts against each other to see who could achieve the most submissions. The unbeaten Timea would take great delight in scissoring her victims, like the beautiful Lada, until they cried for mercy. The older Swede, Tina, had fun using her skills to reduce the voluptuous nineteen-year-old Hungarian, Andrea, to tears. I was besotted with all the fighters. In real life, they were dancers or police-women or students or shopworkers. On tape, they were superwomen, and I envied all of their boyfriends.

Was this a kind of pornography? Probably. Rules-based fights between young women, often but not always topless, were certainly a stimulating spectacle. Some people on the Internet forums considered it a fetish and were able to pinpoint precise moments in their own lives where the fetish had been triggered in them. Perhaps when a babysitter had told them of a make-believe fight that they had participated in that day; perhaps when a sister participated in an actual fight at school; perhaps when their mother had an argument with another at the school gates. I have not been able to identify where my own taste for such a spectacle was born. Isn't it latent in all of us? At school when kids got into fights, everybody would watch, whether they involved boys or girls. Girl fights were much rarer, but not unheard of, although they rarely got past the stage of arguments and posturing. It was more than entertainment. You wanted to know where people stood in the pecking order, and you wanted to assess where you stood too. It was about bragging rights.

When my girlfriend, Rachel, asked whether I had a pornography collection, these were the only tapes I could show her. I had known her for several months – the previous September, she had arrived to teach at the school where I had already been teaching for a few years. We were reaching the stage of our relationship where the vanilla sex was starting to pall, and we were comfortable enough in each other's company to begin sharing our deeper fantasies. Rachel was intrigued by the whole phenomenon of female wrestling, especially when I showed her some of the videotapes that I had purchased from DWW (Danube Women Wrestling), a niche business based in Austria which sold videotapes of East European (mostly Czech) beauties wrestling each other in domestic surroundings. Because most of their matches took places in informal venues such as houses and flats, the genre was known as 'apartment wrestling.'

DWW produced a variety of other match styles, including the Black Sea Amazons, an appropriately named outfit of formidable and ferocious young women who held no-holds-barred ring fights until one of them submitted. Mixed Martial Arts was in its infancy, and female MMA matches were virtually unheard-of, so the Amazons certainly provided entertainment of a sort unmatched anywhere else. Brutal endings were not uncommon.

For the cognoscenti, US-based Crystal produced 'Video Magazines' a couple of times a year. Whilst most of the two hours were packed with filler material - such as grainy amateur boxing matches, storyline scripted fights or female fight scenes from old movies - they usually featured half an hour of real apartment-based girl fights, often without rules, the like of which had never been seen before, or probably since.

A halfway-house between DWW-style wrestling and the brutality of the Black Sea Amazons and Crystal was the style known as catfighting, a genre which was growing increasingly popular among DWW's client base, going by the pattern of their recent releases. This style appealed to me the most, because it consisted of moderately un-trained girl-next-door types going up against each other to find out who would prevail. And whereas wrestling matches could sometimes be a tedious spectacle, dom-inated by technical holds, catfighting added spice to the mixture by allowing hairpulling, body-slapping and occa-sionally, if one was lucky, kicking and face-slapping.

The fights on video became a part of our lovemaking ritual. Rachel and I would watch a fight where she re-sembled one of the participants (there was no shortage of beautiful blonde-brunette fighters in Eastern Europe) and we would fantasise that it actually was her, matched against someone we knew who looked like the video op-ponent. Sometimes it would be another teacher at the school, sometimes a celebrity, sometimes even an older student.

I didn't think I would be able to persuade Rachel to con-sider participating in a real match like this for my entertainment. Whether she offered to put herself up for one because she knew it turned me on, or because she genuinely wanted to step outside her comfort zone and test herself, I will never know. It was probably a mixture of both.

Rachel was almost twenty-six-years old, five foot nine inches tall and approximately 125lbs (57kg). She was sporty, gymnastic and athletic but definitely not someone you would think of as a fighter. The first impression she gave was of a 'nice,' respectable, girl-next-door university graduate in the first stages of a professional career. Well-spoken and attractive, she had never been in a fight in her life. Rachel combined a traditionalist outlook on life with spirituality and humility, but she was neither prudish nor timid. She had spent several years traveling and living abroad before settling into a teaching career back in England, and was proudly independent and fiercely competitive. Anyone who dared to beat her at Scrabble, let alone any physical endeavour, took their life in their hands.

Back in those days, some people really did arrange real matches online. We were looking for a nice 'friendly' wrestling match for a gentle introduction but for all kinds of reasons (age, weight, location) we couldn't find anyone who exactly fitted our idea of the ideal opponent for Rachel.

We did find one girl who ticked nearly every box: Laura. She was a twenty-one-year-old college student who lived reasonably near – we were in the south of England, and she lived near Windsor, a town just to the west of London and about 50 miles from us. Her 'statistics' made her a good match for Rachel as far as height and weight were concerned, and she was apparently new to this too, although she implied in her profile that she may have been in one or two spontaneous fights. Laura had a boyfriend who had also discovered Barb's site and they had been looking online for someone, just as we had. The only point of difference was that she wanted a catfight rather than a wrestling match. To my surprise, Rachel readily accepted.

There were no videocalls back in those days, so we used e-mail to exchange photos of the girls (alongside their respective partners) together with written challenges from both. Rachel wrote on hers *'Can't wait to get to grips with you, Laura!'* The sign that came back from Laura said *'Let's put on a show for these guys. Only one winner,'* (with a smiley face next to it). She seemed 'nice' enough, even if her e-mail communications may have had a bit of an edge to them if you overanalysed them, as I was inclined to do.

The match was set for a wintry Friday evening, at the student house where Laura lived. I discussed the rules with her boyfriend by e-mail and telephone in the weeks leading up to the match and we managed to arrive at a formulation which both girls were happy with. It was something like this:

- Three-minute rounds with five-minute intervals
- Catfight rules: hairpulling, slapping (including to face), kicking allowed; wrestling holds allowed but no throttling or joint locks. No punching, scratching or attacks to genital regions.
- Trash-talking permitted.
- Winner to be decided by submissions or a retirement. Best of at least 7 submissions, with a winning margin of two subs required for victory.

'Trash-talking' meant that the girls could sling insults at each other as a way of generating an atmosphere before and during the match. Catfighting was about passion, and trash-talking was an integral feature of it. We weren't rich by any means, but I and the other guy each put up £100 to make a £200 prize-pot. Winner take all. Both girls agreed to wear leotards for the contest, just like many of the DWW fighters did.

Between making contact and the day of the match, the girls exchanged a few messages with each other over Internet chat, but there wasn't much to it. I and the other guy spent a lot more time speculating together about how the match would go. We were both understandably excited, and we both fancied our girls to win. He seemed a bit more confident than me, but I thought Rachel's sporty background (she was into swimming, netball, dance, gymnastics) would give her a bit of an edge, certainly when it came to stamina. We also decided, from an 'atmospheric' standpoint, not to let the girls meet each other until they were fully attired and ready to fight.

The couple of weeks leading up to the match were fun. As well as discussing the opponent and what tactics Rachel might use, we had several sessions where I taught her a few basic wrestling holds (grapevines, pins, camel clutches) and techniques (for example, how to try to unsaddle an opponent sitting astride you), all learned from studious viewing of the video-fare that was arriving at my house. Rachel was a quick learner.

We were nervous too. When you are engaged in an e-mail discussion with someone about rules for a catfight, it doesn't seem real, but as the day approached, Rachel and I both became apprehensive. What if they were not as pleasant in real life as they seemed to be online? Was Rachel really prepared for the pain that a catfight was likely to bring? We watched some tapes and talked it through, how she would cope when she found herself under pressure. I even wrestled her myself and put her through some painful holds to test how well she might be able to deal with it if the other girl started to get on top. I even trash-talked her.

'Come on, you weakling. You can do better than that! Don't squeal when I twist your arm like that. If you do that when she applies a hold like that to you, she's gonna eat you for breakfast!'

I'm not sure how beneficial it was but it really riled her, and she fought back valiantly, especially when I called her 'bitch'. It was at least heartening to know that she might be able to deal with the rigours that a catfight might bring.

The day arrived. We turned up at their rented student accommodation in the early evening and the guy ushered us in. We learned that Laura was in one of the bedrooms getting ready and that's when he said that, as well as him, another couple in the house wanted to watch if that was okay. We felt a bit bounced into it, but we agreed, and then he showed us into a large double bedroom where this other couple were already sitting on the bed. They were also students and were there to support their friend, but we were okay with it. They got up and left the room so that Rachel could change into her leotard.

At that point it all started to feel very real.

The other guy, Kev, had thought about this a lot, it was clear. Everything was so well-prepared. In one corner of the large bedroom, adjacent to the front wall of the house, was the double bed on which the other couple had been sitting when we first entered. In the three other corners were polystyrene-filled beanbags, large plastic water-bottles next to the two opposite each other, and the entire floor had been covered with duvets. Perhaps he had read the same page on the web that I had about precautions against carpet burns. They must have used every duvet in that house because this was not a small room – perhaps 5 metres by 4 metres, plenty of space for what was about to unfold even if the bed in the corner made the room feel a bit smaller.

Rachel changed into her electric blue leotard and I asked how she felt. Without saying a word, she took my hand and held it up to her chest. Her heart beat wildly.

'Nervous?' I said, looking into her eyes.

'Yeah. Excited too, though.'

I reminded her what we had covered in our training sessions and there was a knock on the door.

'Best to go now if you need the toilet. I'll show you where it is.'

I and Kev had agreed on the phone that once the match was underway, no-one would leave the room until we had a winner, so he showed us along the corridor to a small bathroom and I waited outside while Rachel slipped in. He entered the bedroom opposite and for the first time, I heard Laura's muffled voice,

'What's she like?'

Until that moment, our only communication had been by e-mail (plus one phone call between me and Kev). The voice was young, excited, middle-class. I couldn't help thinking how perfectly matched these two were.

'Yeah, they seem nice. Nothing to worry about, though. I think it's going to be a good night.'

I thought she replied, 'Goodnight Vienna,' but maybe I was imagining it. They moved away from the door and I couldn't make out the rest of the conversation, so when Rachel emerged, we moved back to the match room.

She looked magnificent; her skin glowed as she stood before me, and she smiled back when I told her she was going to win this.

'I don't want you to lose your money,' she said.

Her hair, once blonde, had darkened into adulthood and now was a light brunette with highlights, though they were all natural. It hung loose just below her shoulders as had been agreed. I and Kev wanted a girl-next-door kind of fight, and we were going to get one.

Another knock.

'Ready?' asked Kev.

We nodded. The spectator-couple re-entered, introduced themselves by name, shook hands with us, and sat on the bed expectantly. Kev said that when Laura entered, both girls could face-off in the middle and make sure the rules were crystal clear. We would both be responsible for refereeing the bout, and the guy on the bed, suitably equipped with a whistle, agreed to be the timekeeper. Kev had primed me that during the face-off he would ask each girl if they had anything to say to the other before the fight (he probably got the idea from his own videotapes), so we had worked out Rachel's line in advance.

The doorhandle turned down and the door swung slowly open. Never was there a more expectant moment in my life. In she walked, barefoot in all-black leotard, smiling nervously as she glanced towards Kev. Like Rachel, Laura's arms and legs were toned but not especially muscular. Her dark brunette hair – much darker than Rachel's - fell to about the same length as my girl's. Rachel wore no make-up, but Laura had applied crimson lipstick and her pale, puppy-fat complexion was flawless. She glanced at her boyfriend before looking over to us, and I noticed that as soon as he raised his eyebrows to her in response, her demeanour changed. She was tall, clearly fit, and I saw a steeliness in her eyes that I hoped Rachel had not noticed. The smile vanished and her face was serious when she looked at us.

'Hi. I'm Laura,' she said, lips closed, half-smiling, half-smirking.

Something in the way she carried herself, maybe the way she faced us full-on, conveyed calm self-assurance. You couldn't notice the five-year age difference. Laura looked a little older than her years, Rachel a little younger. If you had not known, you would have said there was no more than a year between them. They could both have passed for twenty-three.

Both girls stared at each other from separate corners of the room for no more than a few seconds, sizing each other up, and we watched on, doing the same, but it felt like a whole minute of uncomfortable silence. Rachel looked across to me and gave me a nod of reassurance, as if to let me know that she was feeling comfortable and that there was nothing to worry about. I noticed that Laura looked at Kev and gave him an equally confident smile. They were both excited.

'Come together, girls,' said Kev, and I stood next to Rachel as he stood next to Laura when they met in the centre of the room.

That's when the electricity started. Face to face, these girls knew they were about to fight each other. There was no backing out now. Although they glanced into each other's eyes briefly, neither could hold the stare. The handshake between them was cursory. It was cute that they didn't know where to look, obviously awkward in each other's company, so they glanced at Kev as he went through the rules, stealing occasional quick glimpses towards me and to each other. Not quite the staredown which Kev and I had hoped for. The rules read, Kev asked if they were clear, reminding them about the £200 prize for the winner. They both nodded, staring intently at each other for the first time.

'Is there anything you want to say, Rachel?' Kev asked.

Rachel delivered her line:

'May the best girl win.'

Man, that line encapsulated the 'fun competition' vibe we were looking for, but we really should have thought about it more carefully. Laura snorted mockingly, and Rachel was visibly deflated.

'What do you want to say to Rachel, Laura?' asked Kev, knowing that his girl had a zinger prepared.

Laura moved her face closer towards Rachel, locked eyes on hers for several seconds and said with a smirk,

'Don't look so scared. I'm not going to hurt you... much.'

Damn, that was good. It was a shock to the couple on the bed too, both of whom gave an audible gasp as she delivered it. Rachel looked surprised. Laura stepped slowly backwards to her corner without breaking the stare; we turned and went back to ours.

'It was just a line,' I reassured Rachel. 'Let's do this.'

That weight of excited expectation one senses in the few seconds before the cup final kicks off, or in the instant before the stalls open in the Derby, was in the room but a thousand times heavier. Rachel's face reddened as the realisation of the impending struggle hit home, and the geeky-looking guy and girl on the bed couldn't contain themselves any longer. I had paid them no attention up to this point, but their apparent neutrality was now shattered as they both cheered loudly,

'Come on Laura! Come on!'

Rachel and Laura locked eyes again. Kev and I took our places next to the couple on the bed, and the geek blew his whistle. It was on.

At this point, the reader may be expecting a round-by-round, blow-by-blow account of what transpired. I am sorry to disappoint. A quarter of a century has passed since Rachel and Laura went up against each other, and it would be disingenuous to pretend that I have an accurate memory of the match as it happened. There is neither video nor photographic record. Shards of memory, some incredibly vivid, form a collage in my mind to create an overall mental souvenir of the fight, but there are details I cannot recall. That evening provided such sensory overload that its intensity is engraved on my mind far more deeply than the precise chronology. I remember the fight's overall trajectory; the pivotal moments; the colour and texture; even some of the dialogue. But I could not honestly tell you the order of submissions or even how many there were.

I have considered using poetic license to present the unfolding of the match in traditional 'catfight fiction' fashion but decided against. This is not fan fiction and to portray it as such would be an injustice to the truth, indeed an affront to the memories of two quite remarkable women.

I may have referred to Rachel and Laura as 'girls' (just as Kev and I referred to them as 'the girls' when we were planning this escapade). What unfolded on that night, however, turned out to be a rite of passage – certainly for Rachel. In some sense, she entered that fight as a girl and emerged from it as a woman. I suspect the same was true for her opponent.

The early part of the match gave no indication of how it would play out. Broad grins broke out on the faces of both girls as they circled each other for the first time, pawing the air, throwing feints. They may not even have touched each other for the first minute. Only the exhalations accompanying their air-slaps broke the silence. It was a dance. We four spectators, perched together atop the bed watched on, mesmerised. No cheering now. It was fun, but it was a contest nonetheless, and we all felt the weight of it. If those slaps had connected, they surely would have hurt.

I noted the solidity of Laura's thighs. Kev had told me that she played hockey, rode and swam. It showed. Her sports were beefier than Rachel's, and I wondered if we might be about to see a battle of power versus agility. I could see what Kev found attractive about her. She was good-looking: not necessarily beautiful in a classical sense, but she was statuesque, and her stupendous figure was accentuated by the tightness of her black leotard. What's more, though she appeared totally feminine, her face conveyed a tomboyish nature. Kev had told me that Laura was extremely competitive whenever she played sport, and he was confident she would be going all-out for the win. She certainly wore the determined demeanour of someone who would 'leave it all in the ring'.

After finally coming to grips with each other, Rachel and Laura soon landed in a rolling maul on the floor, both wrestling for dominance with degrees of success for both. It was exhilarating to see Rachel finally in combat against another woman. Laura may have been slightly more powerful, but Rachel was nimble and slipped away without too much difficulty when those thighs tried to close her in their grip.

The three-minute opener was over before we could draw breath and the geek whistled to signal the first five-minute rest. Laura held out her hand to pull Rachel up from the floor, and they exchanged smiles on the way to their corners. The round may have been little more than horseplay, but Rachel was breathing as if she had just come back from one of her three-mile runs. I checked back over my shoulder – Laura was too. It had taken something out of both, even if it had seemed tame from our vantage point.

As she rested on the beanbag and reached for some gulps of water, I gave Rachel some words of encouragement before realising that everyone in the room was listening. Tactical discussions, if required later, would need to be given sotto voce. Little was said in either corner during the first few intervals of the fight. Both girls rested, Laura confident and self-assured, Rachel more pensive. Between rounds, the girls didn't speak to each other but Kev and I congratulated each other on the way the match was going. This was fun. We shared a whispered vision of turning this into a monthly fight-night, and we were openly complimentary about each other's partners. Laura turned and gave me a broad grin from her beanbag when she overheard how impressed I was with her physique. Rachel pretended not to have heard, but I could tell that she had and she was less than pleased.

Rounds two, three and maybe four continued in similar fashion. Wrestling more than catfighting, both girls enjoying the feeling of their strength exerted upon and resisted by the other. My memory is of seeing more black leotard than blue, suggesting that Laura got slightly the better of it, but Rachel was well in it and I knew that she would grow into the match. My girl had never had a fight in her life before and she was holding her own against an opponent whose demeanour and body-language was formidable. It was all good-natured stuff, and Laura and Rachel were smiling at each other regardless of who was on top. They seemed oblivious to their audience and increasingly focused on dominating each other.

At this point, I sensed Kev starting to become more impatient. Maybe he thought Laura was getting on top and it was time to press home the advantage. We had remarked to each other at the previous interval that the trouble with the format we had settled upon was that it made submissions hard to achieve because positions of dominance were being nullified when the whistle sounded. He glanced over at the timekeeper's watch.

'Only thirty seconds left in this one, Laur. Make it a catfight!' he suddenly implored.

It was the first time that any of us had volubly offered support since that rumble of encouragement which preceded the beginning of round one. Laura was on top in the middle of the room, gradually moving her muscular thighs up to straddle Rachel's breasts, continuing a brief period of dominance for her. I wondered if her apparent lack of technique might make submissions hard for Laura to achieve, though. She was pinning Rachel sure enough, but pins don't win catfights. I couldn't see how Laura was going to extract the four submissions required. On the other hand, Rachel had been trying to technically exploit some of the openings she was being presented with. She had had little success to this point, but I thought the chances would come eventually.

Kev's shout electrified Laura. Instinctively her left hand grabbed a chunk of Rachel's hair, yanking her neck forward towards the crotch of her black leotard. Rachel yelped, in a mixture of shock and pain. Maybe it was the first time in two decades that anyone had pulled her hair – we certainly hadn't practiced it in training. At the same time, Laura's open right palm crashed into Rachel's bare thigh. Laura smiled as Rachel gasped.

'Twenty seconds!' yelled Kev.

The geek-couple on the bed winced, then roared their approval as another slap reddened Rachel's thigh and she was visibly hurt.

'Make it to the end of the round, Rach!' I urged.

The slaps did not come in quick succession, but they carried a lot of spite. Two more caused Rachel's leg to twitch. I was transfixed by the sudden fiery determination on Laura's face. With the ruthless cruelty of a natural born winner, she smiled, sensing that she was hurting Rachel. Rachel grimaced determinedly, taking her pain, determined to hang in.

'Ten seconds!' counted Kev, at the same time as Laura

yelled,

'You might wanna give at this point!'

To my shame, I was torn. Of course, I wanted Rachel to make it to the end of the round, but a part of me did not want Laura's shocking display of dominance to go unrewarded. I felt myself going hard.

Whack.

'Huh? You wanna give?'

Rachel was writhing in desperation. God. Laura looked magnificent but she was beating up my girlfriend!

Four, five, six unanswered slaps in total hit home. Every one must have hurt, but after that first yelp, Rachel did not give Laura the pleasure of hearing another one.

I noticed that the countdown timer on the geek's wrist had reached zero, so I told him in no uncertain terms to blow the bloody whistle.

Irritated that she hadn't obtained the sub, Laura got in one more slap and gently tossed Rachel's head back to the duvet like a piece of litter. Then she rose to her two feet, shook her head in disgust, caught Kev's eyes and laughed. Kev was off the bed, fist-pumping the air, but saying nothing as he joined her in her corner.

'Fuck!' exclaimed Rachel.

She had crawled to her beanbag, which made her injury look worse than it was, where I joined her.

'Fuck! Sorry. Don't say anything yet. Give me a minute.'

She was breathless and her hand shook as she reached for the water-bottle.

I turned around to hear Kev congratulating Laura on what he called a '10-8' round.

'You really sent a message to her at the end there,' he said.

Laura was now too excited to sit and there was colour in her cheeks. She was into it, prowling from wall to wall like a lioness, gulping her water and occasionally looking over to Rachel who was staring back. I could see that there was still plenty of fight left in Rachel, and she was quickly getting over the shock of Laura's onslaught. The mood in the room and the vibe between the two had changed, though. It was not exactly hostile, but any illusion of a friendly rough-and-tumble had evaporated.

Halfway through the interval Rachel was ready to talk. Arms around my neck, she whispered,

'What the fuck do I do now?'

Rachel was a genuinely nice girl. Sporty, competitive, but always played by the rules. The cruel confidence I had seen in Laura made me worry about what might be in store for my girl in the next round. Could she tough it out? I now knew that Laura would not flinch when she had the opportunity to hurt Rachel. Suddenly I found myself questioning whether Rachel could respond in kind. What was I thinking? How the hell had I led her into this situation without knowing if she had the killer instinct that was so badly needed here? If she didn't, I had to get her out of there soon for her own safety.

That's when I said it.

'This is it, babe. You're in a proper catfight now. You have to hurt her, or she's going to hurt you. Can you do it? If not, we may as well head home.'

Kev and Laura heard, for sure, and they heard Rachel's determined response too.

'We're not fucking going home.'

She rose to her feet, pushed me aside and started prowl-ing opposite her opponent, saying nothing but fixing Laura with a glare that said she was going nowhere. Laura stared back, unfazed. Fuck. It was terrific.

'Still two minutes till the next round,' said the geek, afraid that they were going to launch themselves at each other before he was ready.

You could tell they wanted to, so I and Kev instinctively went to place ourselves between them. Kev cupped his hand over Laura's ear and said in a muffled voice,

'Get into her head, Laur. Fuck this bitch up in her head and then she'll crumble.'

He didn't intend for anyone else to hear it. Rachel didn't catch it, but I did.

'What the fuck, Kev?' I said, turning round, shocked by his language.

He looked over, embarrassed at being overheard.

'Come on, mate,' he shrugged. 'You talk to yours and I'll talk to mine.'

'You sure you want to do this?' I whispered to my girl.

'Fuck, yes. Get out of my way.'

She was fired up.

'One minute,' the geek reminded us.

Still standing opposite each other, Laura had her hands on her hips. Looking at the hand-shaped welts she had left on Rachel's thigh, she grinned with satisfaction. She was clearly chuffed with her work and nodded her head in the direction of the damage.

'I've got more where that came from,' she laughed, raising

her eyebrows and looking for a reaction.

Rachel stood her ground, returning the stare, steeling herself.

I and Kev returned to the bed-perch. The atmosphere had soured between us, and he was aware of it.

'No hard feelings, mate, yeah?'

I shook my head in response, saying nothing.

Rachel clenched her fists; Laura flexed her neck and we were ready to go again.

The fight becomes a blur for me at this point.

I know that as soon as the whistle went, Rachel charged Laura and closed her two fists around her opponent's hair. Laura, backed up against the wall, applied the same tactic. My recollection is of both girls standing, locked in a hair-pulling stalemate, each trying to overwhelm the other by pulling her hair to the ground. If they did let go of each other, they soon found themselves back in the same position. This was slow, nasty, attritional stuff - excruciating for fighters and partners alike. Their breathing became laboured and small squeals emanated from both as each one tried to gain the upper hand. As heads ground together, inaudible threats were muttered both ways. After the fight, I asked Rachel what was said, but she couldn't remember. Animosity took root. If anyone had the better of it, it was Rachel, who succeeded in pulling her opponent down further than she was being pulled down herself.

'Come on Rach!' I yelled. 'You've got her hurt. Put your weight on her and tire her out!'

Laura's sturdy legs were strong beneath her, though. Grimacing through the pain, she stayed on her feet, continuing to pull on Rachel too.

'Dig deep, Laur!' exhorted Kev.

It was an ugly, hurtful, visually unspectacular round – but when the whistle blew, tempers frayed. Whatever they had been muttering to each other had ratcheted the tension. Laura let go straight away and exploited the opportunity to slap a surprised Rachel in the face, hard, with her free hand. Rachel came straight back, connecting flush with a peach of a face slap. Laura stumbled sideways, losing her balance and fell. In a flash, I and Kev were off the bed to keep them apart. Maybe we should have let it continue, but we were both so wedded to our cherished format that we didn't want this thing turning into an all-out scrap. I have often wondered what would have happened if we had let it. Embarrassed at having been put down by Rachel, Laura tried to make light of it as she went back to her corner.

'Is that all you got? Really? I hope you've got more than that because you've just landed yourself in a fight, bitch.'

Rachel just laughed at her. Maybe she was thinking back to when I had called her 'bitch' during our trash-talk training session. Now her opponent had used the insult in the heat of battle.

Equal amounts of light and dark brunette strands lay in clumps on the duvets as testament to the damage that had been inflicted during those three gruelling minutes. Rachel's eyes were watering when I got her back to the corner but there was quiet satisfaction from both of us at the way she had handled herself. Maybe she really could 'cat it out' when push came to shove.

Now it was her turn to prowl, re-energised by the hurt she had inflicted and encouraged to see Laura rubbing the sore ear where her slap had connected. The smile on her face told me that she was enjoying this.

The temperature continued to rise. Rachel became more and more psyched. She paced impatiently waiting for the resumption of hostilities and couldn't resist taunting Laura who, still on her beanbag, was checking her scalp and looking more injured than I had previously realised.

'Cheats don't prosper. You push it again and you'll get it straight back from me, bitch.'

I had never seen Rachel say anything with such aggression. This brought Laura to her feet, and Kev had to restrain her.

'Fuck you! You want a catfight or don't you, you stupid cow? We're not playing at it. Fight me or fuck off and leave the money here.'

'Fuck you!' snorted Rachel, increasingly confident that this was going to be her night.

I motioned Rachel to back off and told Kev to get Laura back to her corner. Then we met in the middle and tried to have a conversation out of earshot.

'This is getting out of hand,' I warned him. 'You wanna let them continue?'

'I ain't gonna stop them,' he said, 'and they both want it, don't they? How 'bout we scrap the three-minute round and let 'em fight until we get submissions?'

We checked with our fighters. They wanted it. Boy, did they want it.

As the fight unfolded, Laura escalated the violence and Rachel tried to follow suit. The hairpulling standing clinches continued but now Laura was starting to use her powerful legs to beneficial effect. With hands tied up in each other's hair and Rachel backed up against the wall, Laura's knee thrust hard into the outside of Rachel's welted thigh and she got the response she was wanting. Rachel buckled and squealed, but she didn't drop.

'Oooh, that hurt ya, didn't it?' taunted Laura vindictively, 'Don't cry, baby.'

And then, cruelly, she did it again. A sharp intake of breath from everyone on the bed. Rachel winced.

Taking a step backward, hands still locked in hair, Laura then kick-pushed Rachel in the stomach, sending her slamming back into the wall so that Rachel's head thudded against the plasterboard partition.

'Go on, Laura!' cheered her girlfriend on the bed, unable to restrain herself, 'Smash her up!'

Before she could recover, Laura swarmed Rachel. A stamp-kick to the same thigh and then a knee to her midriff soon had Rachel sagging to the floor. Egged on by her supporters, Laura pulled her over by the hair and, smiling, stood on my girl's stomach, pressing down hard with her foot whilst pulling Rachel's hair with all her might. They were giving everything, thrashing and fighting like wild animals.

Somehow, Rachel got away and made it to her feet, but Laura was onto her and there was nowhere to hide. Rachel, hurt and weakened, was at Laura's mercy and there was no whistle to save her this time. Laura piled in, establishing a front headlock, once again backing Rachel up. A heel kick landed on Rachel's shin, and Laura tightened the hold, grimacing. As Rachel soaked up the punishment, Kev rose to his feet in excitement.

'You've got her, Laur, she's going!'

Guttural noises emanated from the fighters. Rachel was hurt and struggling for breath; Laura was straining every sinew to consolidate her advantage. I could barely watch. With Rachel still caught in the headlock, Laura swung her free arm to land three sickening punches to Rachel's ribcage. She exhaled loudly with the effort as each one pounded in. Lycra was no protection. Rachel sagged, dropping to her knees, her head still locked in Laura's tight grip.

'Hey, no punching!' I shouted from the bed.

The rules we had agreed explicitly forbade body punching.

'Let them go at it' said Kev, happy that his girl was coming out on top.

Laura stopped punching but the damage was done and Rachel found herself on the floor again. This time Laura was merciless, stamping on Rachel's prone body. She was clearly trying to finish it, there and then.

'Come on Kev, kicking and stomping are not the same thing!' I protested, outraged, whilst all hell was breaking loose in the corner of the room.

Each stomp hit its target, and each time Rachel yelped like a wounded animal. Without taking his eyes off the fight, Kev shrugged.

'Have. Some. Of that!' shouted Laura in unfettered rage.

Each word was punctuated by Laura's heel crunching into Rachel's side.

With the final exclamation, Rachel cried,

'Okay! Okay! I give! I give!' and rolled over into her corner.

That may or may not have been the first sub in the fight, but it was the first one that I can remember from this vantage point nearly a quarter of a century later.

Immediately, and unforgettably, Laura turned away from the stricken Rachel and beamed at us all on the bed, alternately pumping her open-palms to the sky in quick, mini fist-pumps. She was sweetness and light again, dancing like a ten-year-old girl, as if those moments of brutality had exorcised her ill-will. Or maybe she was just trying to turn us on. If so, she succeeded beyond her wildest dreams. The whole room, me included, wanted to fuck this supreme creature in her moment of glory. I could barely take my eyes off her, even though the crumpled electric-blue heap she had left on the beanbag was Rachel, who lay curled up facing the wall, her body heaving silently as she choked back tears.

'Let's call it here,' said Kev, looking at me for approval.

I hesitated.

'Maybe. Just give her five minutes to see if she can continue,' I replied, not thinking for one moment that Rachel would, but knowing that she had to have some say in this.

I rushed over to her and crouched down. Welts covered her arms and legs, and her face was starting to swell.

'Are you OK, Rach?'

'Nothing's broken. Give me some time. She's a fucking cheat.'

'I know. Let's just go home. You fought magnificently.'

She looked at me as if I were insane.

'I'm not. Fucking. Done.'

She sat up, grabbed the water from my hand, and inspected her battered body. Kev and Laura, both on their feet, were embracing, as if they thought the contest was over.

'Don't celebrate just yet. It might not be finished,' I called over to them, reluctant to let the match continue but shaken by Rachel's determination that it should.

The spectator couple had made to move off the bed for the first time in an hour but now they stayed to see if there was more drama to come. Kev and Laura looked across, astonished that Rachel might want another round. A look of irritation flashed across Laura's face and then she set about her own line of persuasion.

'Keep it coming if you want,' she said, 'but you should know that I'm only just getting started on her. If she gets hurt that's on both of you,' she threatened, staring point-edly at me. 'Maybe you just want to see me do a number on your girlfriend. Sure thing,' she smiled, 'I'll fuck her up if that's what you really want, daddy.'

She held eye contact with me for a few seconds too long, and then beamed again. For a nice middle-class English girl, she damn-well knew how to be bad.

Kev looked like he wanted us to call it a day and said that Rachel only had two and a half minutes left to get ready for the next round if she wanted the fight to go deeper. Behind me, my girl had already made it to her feet, but I was concerned that she wasn't moving freely, treading gingerly as if her left leg was still suffering from Laura's earlier attacks. Rachel walked around, taking deep breaths, trying to shake it off without letting Laura know the extent of the damage. Gathering her strength and courage, she put her hands on her hips and looked ac-cusingly across to her tormentor.

'We have rules, but you break them, you fucking cheat. If you want to punch bodies, let's do it; if you want to stomp, let's do it. You and I. Are not. Done.'

Without saying a word, Laura glared back, beckoning her mockingly with both hands. In the middle of the room, Kev and I took several minutes to discuss how we could keep a lid on this pressure-cooker fight. I was trying to buy as much time for Rachel to recover as I could.

'If Laura throws a single face punch, that prize-money is off-the-table and I'm stopping it,' I threatened.

Laura heard it and scoffed.

'Still best of seven subs, though, right?' Kev checked.

I nodded.

'No way this is going that long,' he muttered to his girl. 'You can finish her any time you want. One more sends her home.'

In her corner of the room, Laura strutted, menacingly and - I hate to say it – magnificently. She owned the room, and there was no disguising the malice she was nurturing for Rachel. She was getting ready to close the show.

'She's trying to psych you out,' I whispered to Rachel, looking straight into her grey-blue eyes.

Rachel gulped hard.

'You don't have to do this.'

'Yes, I fucking well do.'

'Put it on her then. Make her cry for me.'

Rachel looked straight past me, glaring at her opponent across the room, summoning up hatred, perhaps visualising the violence she wanted to visit on the girl who had just assaulted her and who was now getting ready to do it again.

Trying to intimidate Rachel, Laura moved in closer, stalking her. I sensed her lurking over my right shoulder.

'Boo-fucking-hoo,' she said, deadpan, before swaggering back.

I heard her laughing about it with Kev.

I kissed Rachel's forehead; she nodded, took another swig of water and gritted her teeth. She took three deep breaths. Laura and Rachel now stood impatiently in their respective corners, itching to hurt each other again. Despite our best efforts, no amount of cajoling would persuade them to shake hands. They wanted this thing done, and as Laura had originally predicted, there could only be one winner. It had stopped being a contest. Now it was a fight, pure and simple. However long it took, it needed a finish.

Kev and I took our positions on the bed. The guy with the whistle was no longer needed. 'Fight!' said Kev next to me, and we watched them go at it again, tooth and claw.

I will never know for sure, but my life might have taken a different shape had it not been for the next few minutes. Perhaps Rachel and Laura knew somewhere deep inside that there was more on the line than £200 prize money. Maybe they knew that their self-esteem, the confidence they would take through life, the way they would be forever remembered by the onlookers would be determined by the sound and the fury of the impending moments. I am convinced that what happened directly affected the subsequent story of me and Rachel, but also that of Kev and Laura.

They collided in a sustained fury of frantic slapping. Both

girls' palms connected squarely on the other's body and face, their screams a blend of effort, frustration and pain, and I was relieved to see Rachel fighting her way back into it. Maybe the damage Laura had inflicted was superficial after all. Rachel landed a hard kick of her own against Laura's knee, causing the younger woman to cry out loud - but then Rachel winced, betraying the pain in her own standing leg. Laura noted it.

They broke momentarily, circling, trying to regain breath, both knowing that stamina was running out and that the climax was beckoning. The animosity they had fuelled over the last hour was alight and in full flame. Suddenly, winning seemed insufficient. We willed and exhorted our women to maim each other. It was barbaric, it was visceral, and it was sexy as hell.

Sensing that Rachel was breathing heavily, Laura initiated the next attack, but was punished for it with a blistering slap as she came forward. It sounded like a firecracker had gone off in the room and Laura retreated to the other side of it, clutching her jaw with both hands.

'Fuck!' she exclaimed, shocked and hurt.

'Get her, Rach!'

My blood rose as the tables turned, and I urged my girl forward. Laura was on the back foot, but Rachel was slow to get there and couldn't, or wouldn't, sustain the follow-up. Laura re-grouped, furious and snarling.

Another flurry of hairpulling and slapping led to a rejuvenated Laura backing Rachel into the neutral corner, furthest from the bed. Grinding her down now and sapping my girl's strength, the bodyweight she applied behind her left forearm exerted pressure on Rachel's neck, trapping her between the two walls. From where we sat, the black leotard eclipsed the electric-blue one as Laura started to go to work. She targeted the thigh yet again, with malign intent and ruthless efficiency. Fuck. Multiple heavy knee-strikes found their target and Rachel was helpless to cover up. Taking her time and leaning in, Laura made sure each one landed like a wrecking ball onto the outside of Rachel's upper left leg. Each strike was accompanied by a vicious, grunted exhalation as she invested her full power into Rachel's increasing distress. Rewarded by a crescendo of Rachel's increasingly anguished cries, Laura hammered layer upon layer of hurt onto the same spot. There was nothing superficial about the damage she was wreaking now.

Kev rose to his feet, loving every second of the carnage-in-progress. I was paralysed but we were both rock-hard.

Desperately seeking to protect her thigh, Rachel drew back her leg, only to expose her mid-section to the next phase of Laura's assault. The girl in black lycra clenched her hand into a fist. A vicious punch to the solar plexus drew out the last vestige of resistance from Rachel and her face, or what I could see of it through her hair, contorted with pain. She had no choice but to remain upright, held up by her determined opponent's forearm. Laura followed up ruthlessly, putting maximum force into another thudding punch to the midriff and Rachel's face crumpled, eyes closed, her agony mixed with despair. Half-conscious, she was being brutalised, and Laura was having fun now.

'Oh fuck!' gasped the girl from the other couple, horrified by the raw violence her friend was unleashing and the pleasure she was taking from it.

'Finish her, Laur!' roared Kev.

Sensing the end and showing no mercy, Laura finally re-linquished the forearm; yanked Rachel's head down; with a guttural shout, thrust one last brutal knee into the pit of her stomach; and stood back to marvel at the result of her wanton destruction.

Rachel fell to her knees in the neutral corner and slumped, face-down.

'FUCK yes!!' gasped Laura, in awe of her own work.

Rachel's body lay motionless.

'Fuck. YES!!' Laura screamed in celebration, appreciating the carnage she had wrought.

She was elated at having taken Rachel's consciousness. Like an Amazon, Laura shook both her fists in the air. There was no denying her terrible, sadistic beauty.

It was a couple of minutes before Rachel started to come round. As I administered first aid, I was aware out of the corner of my eye, that Kev had raised his partner's arm in triumph.

'The WINNER! By KNOCKOUT!' he declared to the couple on the bed, unable to contain his pride, and Laura wiggled her bottom in a little dance of celebration.

'Fuck off, Kev.' I muttered under my breath.

I checked Rachel over. Every limb carried a souvenir of Laura's violence, but the only significant injury was the damage that Laura had wrought on that left thigh. It flared as angry as the fight, and Rachel flinched when I touched it. Within a couple of days, a huge patch of purple would serve as a two-week-long reminder of the beating she had taken at the hands and knees of the younger woman. Across the room, they were calling it a beatdown.

I propped Rachel up in a sitting position, her legs outstretched, in the corner where Laura had rendered her unconscious. She started to hyperventilate. Trying to calm herself, she exhaled deeply, staring catatonically at the ruffled, hair-strewn duvets. Proffering the water bottle every so often, I waited for her to recover from the shock of that brutal ending. I tried to process the enormity of what had just happened, reliving the final moments of the contest in my head. The girl in the black leotard had laid out my sweet angel in the most devastating and stunning display of female brutality I had ever witnessed.

Laura sauntered across in conciliatory fashion and leaned over, still breathing heavily. Beads of perspiration glistened on her upper lip. The long-standing bulge in my crotch, for which she was responsible, swelled again as her breasts lowered to form a lycra-clad valley next to my face. She couldn't disguise her pride at what she had just done. Her superiority was unquestionable.

'No hard feelings. That was a great battle. I really enjoyed it.'

Twenty-four years later, I can still hear the emphasis she put on the word 'really.' What the fuck?

Laura held her outstretched hand towards Rachel, who took it limply, unable to sustain eye contact with the girl who had just beaten her up. The handshake was even more cursory and insincere than the one which had begun the evening. Uncomfortable with the awkwardness, Laura smirked and returned to her friends across the room, shrugging her shoulders.

Rachel raised her hand to mask her crumpled face and burst into tears.

'I'm sorry,' she whispered.

I took her in my arms and held her. Maybe the embrace lasted two minutes, maybe it was fifteen. We said nothing. Contradictory feelings tumbled inside me, but the overwhelming one was to protect her. Too late, I know. Behind me I could hear Kev and Laura whispering and sniggering awkwardly, conscious they were intruding on private grief.

When I looked up, the other couple had gone, and Kev and Laura were locked in their own, more passionate clinch over on the bed. It was obvious that we were delaying the progression of their celebration to its inevitable carnal conclusion in the arena of her triumph. They broke off when I rose to my feet. The air hung heavy with pheromones and sweat.

I collected Rachel's things, handed the money to Kev, and without speaking, we assisted Rachel as she limped, shuffling like an invalid, towards the doorway and the stairs. Her face was puffy and red from the crying, her eyes half-closed from the humiliation. Laura lingered in the background on the landing, frequent smirks to Kev revealing her jubilation and pride at the indelible wounds she had carved on Rachel's body and soul.

Rachel couldn't make it down the stairs on her own so, still in her leotard, I picked her up and carried her to the car, wrapping her in a couple of blankets to protect her from the winter cold.

There were no goodbyes. As Kev handed me her things, he just said,

'Let's have a rematch one day.'

It was an ignominious exit. We didn't know then that I would be back three weeks later, albeit without Rachel.

The journey home was virtually wordless, with Rachel shaking and sobbing in the passenger seat for much of the hour-long drive. I will never know how much of it stemmed from the physical beating she had taken from Laura, how much from the emotional humiliation, and how much from an unconscious suspicion that she had begun to lose me. Her injuries, mental and physical, would take a long time to heal. I wondered if I should take her to a hospital but quickly discounted the idea. It would raise too many awkward questions. My eyes on the road, I tormented myself by imagining Laura and Kev's post-fight copulatory celebrations. I wanted it to be me, making love to Rachel's conqueress in the room where she had annihilated her. Laura had won the fight, and a lot more besides. It was Darwinian and cruel, but my sperm craved her superior eggs.

CHAPTER 2:
GUY TIME

Saturday's early-morning traffic was light. I rang the doorbell. The sound of excited squeals emanated from inside the house. Footsteps descended and the door opened.

There she was, but not as I had expected. It was bizarre that I had pictured her standing on the threshold in a black leotard. Today, she was dressed in blue jeans and a pink t-shirt with a cartoon cat on it. Cute, friendly, even innocent. Nothing to suggest that only three weeks previously, she had beaten my girlfriend to a pulp.

'You came, then?' she said impishly.

'Kev said he thought you might back out.' I recognised that smirk. 'Come on in.'

She led me into a small, modern kitchen. I could hear people moving about overhead.

'Kev upstairs?'

'He'll be here soon. They're just getting it ready.' She motioned upwards.

'Who are 'they'?'

'My housemates. I'll introduce you when they come down. They'd like to watch if that's OK with you. Coffee?'

'I thought you lived here with Kev?'

Her jeans clung tightly to her figure as she leaned over to fill the kettle.

'Christ, no! That would really hamper my style. This is a girlie house.'

She turned and smiled. I gazed at her, shocked by her apparent transformation from hellcat to hostess, but never quite able to forget what she had done. I couldn't help myself.

'You really fucked up Rach.'

'Thanks. The pleasure was all mine.'

She beamed with a mixture of pride and happiness at the memory. Her inner hellcat was stirring.

'Can that bitch walk properly yet?'

I hadn't seen Rachel since Thursday. We didn't live together, and I hadn't told her of my whereabouts this weekend. Three weeks after Laura had inflicted them, the bruises on her thigh – and elsewhere – were now yellowed and fading. Rachel had struggled to walk normally for a week after the fight. It had happened at the start of the half-term break, so she kept away from friends for the whole week - partly so she didn't have to fabricate stories about her injury, and partly because Laura had fucked up her mind as well as her body.

The day after the fight, Rachel had fumed about how 'that fucking bitch' who was now making me coffee had cheated. According to her, I had let her down by not stopping the fight when it started to get out of hand. She was sure that Kev would have stepped in if the boot had been on the other foot. It meant I didn't care for her as much as she thought I did, and she needed space to think about things.

Depression descended in the weeks that followed. No matter how much I spoke in admiration of her courage and fighting spirit, Rachel felt like a loser. The vindictiveness behind the destruction was also hard to shake. As someone who made friends easily and warmly, Rachel couldn't come to terms with the vitriol directed towards her by Laura. She cried more frequently than I had known in the six or seven months of our relationship, and barely raised her eyes. An early spring was breaking out all around us, but Rachel's soul was frozen in a late winter that had blown in bitterly with Laura.

'She's doing OK,' I lied.

Uninterested in my reply, Laura moved closer.

'No offence, but I wanted to fuck her up and I did. She reminded me of a cry-baby I knew at school and she just rubbed me up the wrong way. So...not sorry. I'm not normally like that.'

She smiled unapologetically, shrugged and tilted her head in a show of belligerence. We both knew she would do it again if she could. I still wanted her.

Laura had moved so close to me that her breasts, through her t-shirt, were lightly brushing my chest, and my arms could not resist moving down to the arch of her back, pulling her into me. She didn't resist and draped her arms around my neck. I recalled how decisively her body had prevailed over the other body that I knew so well. Soon I was entangled with the girl-banshee who had felled Rachel, kissing the mouth that had smirked at her injuries; running my hands over the buttocks that had powered those crippling knee-strikes. Laura broke away before my guilty passion overtook us both.

'We shouldn't. I'm supposed to be on Kev's side.'

She went back to spooning instant coffee into two cups. Her legs and bum filled her jeans perfectly.

'How serious are you two?' I asked.

'Not very. Friends with benefits. Why?'

'Because I'm thinking of stealing you from him.'

She threw back her head and laughed.

'I don't belong to anyone. I like the idea of you guys fighting over me, though, and I'll be the prize for this fight, if that's what you want. Winner gets to fuck me straight after, yeah? But you don't get to take your trophy home.'

Then the cruel smile flashed across her face.

'I'd like to see the look on that bitch's face if you did, though.'

There was something irresistible about her need to shock - a shock that was only amplified by the glorious cut-glass accent with which she delivered her contempt.

I wasn't sure if she was winding me up. She placed the cups on the table and we sat down.

'You're serious about us fighting for you as the prize?' I asked.

'Why not?'

'Because you want to fuck me? Or because you want to fuck up Rach even more?'

She had no qualms.

'Both. I won't tell her if that's what you're worried about, though. Fuck her. I only fuck winners, though.'

'I can handle myself. Are you doubting me?'

'Fifty-fifty. I have to support Kev out of loyalty but only

because I've known him longer. Besides, I might want you to win me off him. Wendy says she'll be in your corner if you want someone there.'

'Fine by me. I know you want me to win, deep-down.'

She smiled, bit her lower lip and her eyes confessed even if her lips didn't.

'I always end up with the winner. May the best man win, eh?' she said.

I had all the motivation I needed.

There were footsteps on the stairs and two girls, both in blue jeans and t-shirts, entered the kitchen.

'Here's Wendy and Mel. You remember Mel.'

I did remember Mel, just. She was the geeky girl to whom I had paid so little attention three weeks' earlier. She actually wasn't that geeky. It must have been geek-by-association with the presumed boyfriend who had acted as timekeeper that night.

'Hi. Nice to see you again. Would it be too cheeky to ask if me and Wendy could watch later? Just the two of us.'

It was cool with me. A fight with another guy in front of an audience of three young women. What's not to like?

'As long as you're cheering for me, there's no problem.' I joked.

Mel smiled and looked down, embarrassed to sustain the eye contact. She was cute. Every girl I looked at over the last two months had been a fantasy opponent for Rachel, and Mel was no different. I imagined her standing in the opposite corner, dressed in t-shirt and panties. A 5'4" brunette, she was more voluptuous than Rachel and Laura. Her probable D-cup breasts and rounder figure meant she was more-or-less in the same weight class, though. I hadn't noticed her sex appeal on my first visit, but it was there, just under-stated.

Mel apologised and said she would stay neutral 'just to keep things fair' because Wendy had offered to be in my corner.

'It's just an offer,' interjected Wendy, engaging me for the first time, 'I know your girlfriend couldn't make it and I thought it would even things up as Laura's obviously supporting Kev. It's up to you, though. No pressure.'

'I would be honoured. Thanks.'

Of the three girls I was sharing the room with, Wendy was the most classically beautiful. All three young women were refined, their accents suggesting they had benefitted from a private education, but Wendy had total poise. With full lips, thick auburn waves of hair that tumbled onto the shore of her shoulders and an impeccable figure, she oozed class. Her voice was husky, and she spoke in that slow, self-assured drawl favoured by the elite. I could imagine her adorning the 1920s with a cigarette holder between her fingers. My fantasy transformed into a pre-fight stare-down between her and Rachel. Wendy's figure was every bit as impressive as Laura's and Rachel's, and an extra inch of height, maybe two, as well as generous breasts – easily a C-cup - might have given her a kilo or two weight advantage over both.

'Don't go getting too friendly with him,' warned Laura with a twinkle in her eye, 'Let's not forget who they're going to be fighting for.'

Laura had already assumed my agreement to her as the prize on offer. Perhaps my unspoken assent was obvious. Mel and Wendy both registered surprised.

'Really? Wow!' said Mel, glancing at me for verification.

'Wow, indeed,' echoed Wendy, deadpan.

She seemed less than impressed. Mel asked about Rachel and I said she was bearing up.

'I thought she was your girlfriend…,' she said, half-accusingly.

'I'm not sure what we are anymore,' I confessed.

She seemed to accept it.

'That's a shame. Do you think she will do another cat-fight?'

'Who knows? If she did, I doubt I would let her anywhere near Laura again.'

Laura laughed, pleased with the verbal submission.

'Why don't you tell him what you're really thinking?' said Laura, slyly.

There was a moment's silence. Mel looked at me, tentatively. I guessed what was coming. When one woman senses weakness in another, it is often regarded as an opportunity.

'You know, ever since Laura's catfight, we've all been rolling around a bit with each other upstairs most nights, and I'd quite like to try it for myself, you know, a proper catfight. We've been wrestling, but we can't do full-on catfights like Laura had with Rachel because we're friends. I just wondered, you know, if Rachel ever thought about doing another one…'

I noted the implication - that it would be impossible for this triumvirate ever to expand their friendship circle to include Rachel. Mel's proposal was tempting but I didn't want Rachel to become a punchbag for anyone who fancied their chances against her. I couldn't see her fighting again after that torrid first experience, anyway.

'Perhaps I'll pass on the challenge when she's ready for it,' I said, making no promises. 'I hope you're not as brutal as Laura. I guess she comes out on top when you have your roll-arounds, right?'

Laura preened when she heard that I placed her at the top of the pecking order. She had earned it.

'They're both better than me, to be honest, but I'm learning. I even had Laura in a camel clutch yesterday,' she grinned.

I looked at Laura, imagining her discomfort as, in my fantasy, Mel cranked her neck back towards those ample breasts.

'It was just practice,' she retorted, dismissively.

Wendy glimpsed across at me with a quick smile, raising a sceptical eyebrow.

'So anyway,' asked Wendy, eager to change the subject, 'are my first aid skills going to be required today?'

'Never hurts to have a medic on the scene,' joked Laura. I think she was joking.

It was a good question. We hadn't properly considered the rules under which Kev and I would be fighting. I was here at less than 24 hours' notice because Kev had telephoned the day before to say that Laura wanted to see us take each other on. Excited at the prospect of seeing her again, I didn't hesitate.

'I actually told him that I wouldn't have another fight for him unless he did one for my entertainment first,' she explained, 'And I thought it would be pretty cool to have you as his opponent.'

I wondered whether that was the only ruse Laura could think of to get me back in her general vicinity. It would have been simpler, though admittedly much less interesting, if she had simply called.

'What would count as entertainment?' I asked the room in general.

They didn't want blood.

'Why not use the same rules as before?' suggested Mel.

'Before or after she started cheating?' asked Wendy mischievously, who must have received an accurate account from Mel of the earlier fight.

I liked Wendy's attitude. Unlike Mel, she was forthright and enjoyed getting under her friend's skin. Their mutual respect and affection were obvious, however.

'Fuck off, Wend. It was a catfight.'

Wendy sniggered.

'Wish I could have been there to see it.'

'Same rules as me and that bitch of yours, then?' Laura clarified, looking at me for confirmation.

I still hadn't heard her refer to Rachel by her name.

'Body-punching, knees, kicks, yah?' she asked.

'If it's alright with Kev, it's alright with me.'

'Let's keep to three-minute rounds though. I want this to last.'

I nodded.

'Kev wants rounds to continue after a submission. He says if you're not ready to pick up before a ten-count, it should count as a knockout. What do you say?'

I remembered how Kev relished pronouncing the word when Rachel was lying on the bedroom floor, unconscious. Under the current proposal, Rachel's defeat would have been less excruciating – it would not have gone beyond the first submission. I wanted to knock Kev out. Although we had hit it off quite well when we were arranging the match for Rachel and Laura, I was still disappointed with the way he had conducted himself during the fight as well as afterwards, and I wanted to avenge Rachel. I assented. It didn't even occur to me that Kev might knock me out.

The doorbell rang.

'That's him. I don't want you seeing each other before we're in the room together. You go up and get changed. I'll tell him what we've decided. We'll start in about half an hour, yeah?'

She shooed me upstairs, clearly excited by the scenario she had engineered.

Wendy led the way, unbidden. We climbed the stairs together before Laura opened the front door to my erstwhile partner-in-crime and soon-to-be opponent.

The room was set out as it had been when I had first entered it with Rachel. The duvets sprawled smooth and invitingly on the floor, beanbags in two corners of the room, bottles of water next to two of them. I gazed at the neutral corner where Laura had battered Rachel senseless and remembered. The ambience was different, perhaps because this contest was going to take place in the daytime. It was mid-morning and the open curtains let in early spring sunshine. Trees in the street outside the window were just beginning to unfurl their leaves.

Wendy was perceptive.

'Strange feeling?'

'I didn't expect to be back, ever, let alone so soon.'

'Was it as awful as Laura and Mel described it? The way it ended?'

'Pretty devastating. Laura's spiteful.'

Wendy nodded.

'I think she'd take that as a compliment. Why didn't you stop it?'

She was unapologetically direct. That question had haunted me for three weeks and I still didn't have an answer. I shrugged.

'I was mesmerised.'

'And what about today? Do you want me to stop it if you get beaten up? Do you want Laura to stop it if Kev is getting hurt?'

I looked into the neutral corner and contemplated the possibility.

'Only if we're incapable of submitting.'

Rachel had taken her punishment and I felt an obligation to put myself in equal peril. Perhaps it was an act of penance: either for what I had put her through, or more likely, for the betrayal I was contemplating if I came through.

'If that's what you want. I'm not a huge fan of Kev, but I don't want either of you getting hurt. It would lower the tone of the neighbourhood.'

She was an English rose.

'I just want to win well, for Rachel's sake and for mine.'

It felt disingenuous as soon as I said it.

'Well, I'll be rooting for you,' she assured me.

It was good to know that I would have her support. I took my lycra trunks out of my carry-bag and tossed them onto the beanbag in the farthest corner, the one which had been Rachel's. They were electric blue, for Rach.

'And you're really going to fuck Laura if you win?'

I thought of her, downstairs. She still had that aura. Her body, her attitude and her accomplishment made her irresistible to me. My desire was every bit as strong as it had been in the minutes following her knockout of Rachel. Evolution's a bitch.

'You think I'm a prick, don't you?'

'None of my business. I can begin to understand it. Winning is an aphrodisiac and you guys have a lot of testosterone to deal with. Anyway, it's not as if you and your girlfriend are going to be heading down the aisle any time soon. I hope not, anyway. I'll let you get changed. Back in a minute.'

I was alone in the room for the first time. I changed into my blue trunks, kept my black t-shirt on and packed my other clothes away into the carry-bag. The ghosts of Rachel and Laura replayed their bitter conflict in every corner. I stood on the spot where Laura had towered over Rachel's body with her hand raised. Visualising the fight with Kev, I began to limber up. He wouldn't catch me cold.

Wendy knocked on the door and opened it before I could answer.

'They'll be ready in about ten.'

She re-entered, looked me over and nodded. We made eye-contact and I sensed her approval.

'I'm kind of looking forward to this. I've not seen a proper fight between guys before. Girls' school, you know,' she added by way of explanation. 'If I'm already getting butterflies inside, I can only imagine what must be happening with you.'

She was as disarming as she was beautiful.

'You take part in the roll-arounds with Laura and Mel, don't you?'

She nodded. I had the impression she was almost too embarrassed to hear herself admit it out loud.

'You get nervous beforehand?'

'God, yes. And those are only friendlies. It's an adrenalin rush, I get that.'

'Laura does friendlies?'

Wendy stared out of the window. I stared at her behind. It was a comfortable silence.

'Mel sounds like she's ready for something more competitive.'

'Do you think she'd have a chance against Rachel?' Wendy enquired, turning around, genuinely intrigued.

I didn't know what to say. I had never seen Mel fight and I found it quite difficult to imagine. But hey, fantasy catfighting was my 'thing' and so I gave it some serious consideration.

Rachel would start favourite, I ventured. Maybe Mel would have learned a lot from her friendly roll-arounds in that very room, though, and if she started to get some success, it's possible Rachel might fold if the memory of her fight with Laura still plagued her. Especially if Mel cranked up the hatred to Laura-like levels; even more so if

Laura herself was in attendance. But overall? My money would have to be on Rachel.

'What about me? You think I could take her?'

Wendy smiled provocatively, widened her stance, raised her fists like a boxer, and invited me to consider her prospects.

'Rach? I think you'd have a better chance than Mel. Rach is fit, though, and now she knows what it's like to be in a proper fight. If she got into another one, she would benefit from that experience.'

'We're all bitches deep-down inside,' replied Wendy enigmatically.

There was a touch of menace about her but she kept it very well-hidden beneath that sophisticated veneer. It made me like her even more. I wasn't sure I could ever risk Rachel in a catfight again even if she wanted to. I discounted the possibility. Lightning doesn't strike twice.

'And Laura? You think she beats me?'

Wendy continued to prod. We smiled at each other, deliciously, knowing we were both contemplating an impossibly fantastic match-up.

'Well?'

She was impatient to know what I thought.

'If you saw what she did three weeks ago, you would think she beats anybody. She's a hellcat.'

Wendy made the sound of a cat snarling and scratched the air with her pretend feline paw.

'I would give her a good fight, but she's my friend so we'll never know.'

The question hung open and unanswered in my mind for

decades. Laura popped her head round the door, visibly excited as the contest drew near.

'Ready? Kev's nearly done. He'll be along shortly.'

Mel entered and went to join Wendy on the same bed from which I had once been a spectator. Wendy stretched out her long, pixie-booted legs, tossed back her hair, moved it away from her eyes, and prepared for the spectacle of her first 'guy-fight'. As I stood in my corner, we caught each other's eye and exchanged a smile. Mel ogled me shamelessly. She was on a pillow, one leg underneath her, another pillow held against her chest, exactly as before. Unaware of her body language, she licked her lips. I winked at her. Catching herself, she blushed and giggled.

Laura stood in the middle of the room, a handwritten list of rules in her hand, taking me in. She too was absorbed by the hunk in trunks and t-shirt who stood ready to do battle for her. I had never felt so desired.

The door opened and in walked Kev, confident and brash. Their attention immediately switched to him and the bulge in his speedos testified to his own arousal.

'Alright mate?' he nodded from across the room. 'How's Rachel?'

'She's alright.'

I stayed where I was, adopting a wide stance to appear imposing. How does one make pleasantries in these circumstances?

Kev was about 5'9", a couple of inches shorter than me. I guessed he was 180lbs, giving me a 10lb weight advantage. His hair was short-cropped, blondish brown, a number 8 perhaps. Though his frame was slightly smaller than mine, his body was just as muscular. He looked like he lifted. He probably donned a tan from May to November, but this was March, and his skin was as pale as mine. If I had not known he was a college student, I would have guessed him to be a manual worker of some sort. I wondered how someone like him had managed to infiltrate the social circle of three sophisticated middle-class girls. Perhaps they liked a bit of rough. Not knowing my background, perhaps that's how they viewed me too.

Kev enjoyed boyish good looks, at least in comparison to mine - a twenty-one-year-old going up against a twenty-nine-year-old. His all-black speedos were skimpier than the ones which clung to my thighs. On his t-shirt was a WWF wrestler I did not recognise. Pro wrestling's scripted nature held zero appeal for me. Across his shirt was emblazoned the word: 'KNOCKOUT!'

It suddenly hit me that I had never asked whether Kev had trained in any combat sport before. I had no such training, and if he had, I would soon be in deep trouble. What the hell was I thinking not to have checked?

'Get ready, guys, and come to the centre,' commanded Laura.

We divested and threw our t-shirts into our corners. The girls giggled nervously and watched, spellbound, as we strutted across and shook hands in the centre of the room. We both knew we were turning them on. It was a buzz.

I worked out with weights too and, though I must have appealed to a slightly more mature demographic, I sensed my muscularity was contributing to the sexual tension. They had him down as the boy-next-door whilst I was probably cast as the villain of the piece. How could it be otherwise? At nearly thirty years old, I was virtually an alien to them, albeit an exotic one, and though they were too polite to say so, they must have thought me callous for what I had allowed to happen to Rachel. Women have 'a thing' for villains, though, so I played up to it.

His hairless, sculpted torso bumped up against my more hirsute chest. It was theatrical and we both knew the script. Close up, we stared malintent into each other's eyes. I had two inches on him and I made sure he knew it. He exhaled mint from the gum he was chewing. This guy had told Laura to fuck up my girlfriend the last time that I saw him, and she had obliged. I was going to get even with that motherfucker.

The bulges in our crotches made accidental contact as we moved closer to intimidate, an early skirmish in the impending battle. In our silence, we heard the quickening of the girls' breathing, and enjoyed the sensation of their eyes trained on us like lasers as they tried to decide who they wanted.

Laura went through the rules, and we maintained the face-off. The girls, on tenterhooks, grew ever hotter for us. Laura fanned her face with her hand, theatrically.

'Guys, this is a best-of-seven submission wrestling contest, with a two-sub margin needed for victory. Rounds will last three minutes with breaks of five minutes. You may use wrestling holds; you may body-punch or slap; you may kick; knee-strikes are also allowed. You may pull hair. BUT: No strikes to the face; no joint locks; no biting or gouging; no choking; no attacks to the balls. After a submission, you have ten seconds to be ready to resume the match or you will be counted out. I am the referee, and you will obey me. Clear?'

We consented.

'I am also the prize, so you are fighting for ME!'

Laura looked at each of us in turn and beamed.

Addressing me, she asked, 'Is there anything you want to say to Kev?'

I stretched out my hand.

'Let's make it a fun, fair contest.'

My grip was stronger than his.

'Kev?' asked Laura.

'Good luck, mate. You might need it.'

We paced backwards to our corners. I glanced at Wendy who nodded at me, her fists clenched to her bosom.

'Fight!' said Laura, standing back from the centre of the room.

It was on again.

If I find it difficult after a quarter of a century to remember a fight I observed, I find it next to impossible to remember the details of one I was actually in. Even the day after the fight I would have struggled to piece together the chronology of what happened. As before, shards of memory persist, but they form a much more ill-defined collage than the one I was able to piece together for Laura and Rachel's encounter. When I was in the firing line, everything was instinctive; I had a narrow range of focus, often obscured; my time-focus was on what was going to happen in the next second. Very little went into memory.

I will have to content myself by relating those fragments which have stayed with me.

As with Laura and Rachel, the contest mostly took the form of wrestling, certainly at the outset. When dominant, I was reluctant to use the more aggressive moves available to me because I was satisfied with the inroads I had made. Why take a risk by moving the goalposts? Similarly, when under pressure, I was reluctant to utilise more aggressive moves, knowing that they would probably be used back against me from a position of strength. It must have been the same for Kev as we were both content to wrestle for the most part.

Kev was strong but I was stronger. As muscular as he may have been, he hadn't yet grown into his adult strength, and I had. If the match had taken place six or seven years later, he may well have over-powered me.

Kev showed no sign of having been trained and, despite his interest in professional wrestling, was no more technically adept than I was, which is to say, not at all. The match became about domination rather than trying to extract submissions with our limited skillsets. If we couldn't obtain submissions from each other, then at least we could demonstrate our superiority - to each other and to our aroused audience - by being on top the longest.

Laura was a more involved ref than I or Kev had been during her match with Rachel. She stayed on her feet, following us round the room. Though careful to keep out of harm's way, she looked to get close-up on the action whenever she could. Though notionally on Kev's side, she didn't support him vocally during the rounds themselves.

Much of the action took place on the floor, and we each enjoyed periods of dominance. Three-minute rounds were draining and at the end of each round, I gratefully returned to my corner to catch my breath. Laura joined Kev in his corner during the interval breaks.

After the first round, as I swigged water on my beanbag, Wendy ambled over languorously, more from a sense of duty than because she knew how to be useful.

'Cool, you survived that round,' she said cheekily, implying her surprise. 'What am I supposed to do? I've never done this before.'

She turned round to look at the opposite corner by the door. Laura was standing, her back to us, hips swaying from side to side, as she whispered encouragement to Kev.

'Just stand there and look pretty. It will rejuvenate me,' I flirted.

Rachel had disappeared from my mind. Wendy laughed.

'Oh, I'm the ring-girl, am I? I thought I was supposed to be your trainer or something.'

'Well, I'll listen to any tactical insight you've got,' I said in jest.

'OK, this is my advice.'

She leaned down, just as Laura had done in the same room three weeks earlier, and now I was conscious of Wendy's breasts too. They had a stimulating effect, as did the sensation of her breath on my ear.

Cupping her hand, she whispered conspiratorially, 'Tell him there's a wasp in the room, and when he goes to look at it, you can knock him out.'

'Perfect. Why didn't I think of that before?'

She smiled beautifully, pleased with her nugget of wisdom, then turned around and sashayed back to the bed. I looked forward to the intervals just to catch time with her.

Kev tired as our contest continued and I started to dominate, wrestling him down and using my weight and strength advantage to nullify him. At some point, I managed to mount him, achieve a reverse headlock and turn him so that my back was on the duvets with my legs wrapped round his waist, his arms pinned up by his shoulders. I applied a massive scissor-squeeze and he gasped. Peering over the bed, Wendy sent encouragement in her characteristically under-stated tones.

'I think he's under pressure. Do it again,' she oozed in her calm, husky voice.

I kept squeezing and after trying to hold out for a few more seconds, Kev tapped. A round of applause ensued. These girls were such a refined wrestling audience! Then Laura remembered she was supposed to be counting. Kev was up and ready to go again by the time she reached five, and we wrestled out the remainder of the round.

'Nicely done, Hulk,' Wendy approved, as she slunk up to me during the interval, 'Shove up.'

It was unorthodox for a fighter/cornerman dynamic, but we sat next to each other on the beanbag. I put my hand on hers.

'Give me your energy,' I joked.

It was the first time I ever used that line. I have used it several times since. It never fails.

'Yeah, I think I can feel something leaving my body,' Wendy responded, eyes flitting upwards as she interlocked fingers with me.

Laura turned around and shook her head, tutting at Wendy.

'Just doing my job!' she shrugged, proclaiming her innocence, and rose to her feet, returning to the bed like a cat-walk model.

Laura displaced her annoyance at Wendy's over-familiarity with me by taking it out on the hapless Kev. It worked. He came out fired-up.

Our contest may not have reached the heights of brutality that made Laura's display against Rachel so memorable, but as I increasingly overpowered him, Kev ramped up the stakes. I bundled him over to the bed and was on top. As we tumbled towards them, Wendy and Mel retreated to the head of the bed and watched from close quarters as I attempted in vain to apply a camel clutch. His feet still on the floor at the foot of the bed, Kev managed to wriggle out from between my legs and reversed the situation. Now he was dominant, pinning me chest-down on the bed with a knee planted in my back. That's when the body-punching began. I felt the first blow to my right shoulder blade and then a second to my right kidney. They hurt – a lot.

A metre away, Wendy saw me suffering.

Ecstatic to see her man with a chance of evening the score, and perhaps still annoyed by my temerity with Wendy during the interval, Laura temporarily lost her referee's impartiality.

'Come on Kev! Work him over! Show him who's the fucking boss!'

Three more heavy punches to my side made me yell out in pain. I couldn't move and I knew there were more blows coming my way if I just stayed there.

'Ok! I give!' I submitted meekly and rolled onto the floor, clutching my side. It stung like hell. Was it really going to end like this?

Laura started the count immediately.

'One! Two!'

I tasted that bitter blend of ignominy and pain that Rachel must have experienced.

'Three! Four!'

Kev strutted round the room, fist-pumping in the air. I rose to one knee, wincing.

'Five! Six!'

'Get up!' Wendy urged, concern in her honeyed voice, 'Get up!'

'Seven!'

Kevin struck a bodybuilding pose for Mel and Wendy.

'Eight!'

Despite the searing pain in my side, I beat the count as Laura reached nine.

'Thirty seconds left in the round,' called Mel, the ever-diligent timekeeper.

Kevin was on me immediately, applying a front headlock and frogmarching me back to the corner where Laura had finished Rachel. A cacophony of shouting emanated from all three girls, but I was oblivious to whom their exhortations were directed. I hung on, soaking up more punches before Mel finally blew the whistle to end the round.

'One submission each!' announced Laura excitedly as Kev strutted back to his corner where he received a high-five from her.

I slumped onto the beanbag, aching.

'Sorry to break this to you, but I think you just lost that

round. You were doing so well, too.'

Wendy's sympathy was couched in irony. I was disappointed in myself for having let my lead go so easily, and on top of that, Wendy and Laura had seen me humbled.

'Give me your hand again,' I said to her.

'Have another energy transfusion. Maybe it will work this time. Time to see what you're made of, I suppose.'

She had a knack of saying the right thing in few words. Kneeling before me, she took my palm in hers and I contemplated the rings on her index and middle fingers as I waited out the pain, recovered my breath and rested. We said nothing.

After a couple of minutes, I let go her hand, climbed to my feet, and paced in the corner to let Kev know that I was still a force to be reckoned with. On the other side of the room, he was canoodling with Laura, his hands sprawled on the arch in her back that my hands had caressed just an hour before. She pressed her palms lightly against his chest, giggling as he leaned in. Her instructions were clear.

'If you want me, you have to finish him.'

She caught sight of me watching, pleased that I had noticed their display of affection. They broke off and Kev turned back to face me, head high, hands on hips, making himself wide, trying to intimidate. I strode to the middle of the room and mirrored his power stance back at him. Laura interspersed to stop hostilities resuming prematurely and she looked me up and down, trying to gauge what I had left.

In my mind's eye, I saw her beating up Rachel.

'Remember these next few minutes, Laura. I'm taking

you off him and sending him home.'

Seeing her in Kev's arms again had riled me. He was getting it, and so was she.

No fucking around now. We came out, fists raised but slightly lowered, shielding our bodies. A hard left jab through Kevin's guard caught him in the centre of his chest and it was his turn to wince. I might not have known much about wrestling technique, but I knew how to punch. He threw a right hook in retaliation, but it fell short as I stepped back, and he fell forward. My right counter plunged into his mid-section. He doubled-up, and I surged forward, applying a tight front headlock from where I rained lefts into his side, hard enough that the pain vibrated through my knuckles and wrist. Kev reached down to try and topple me. I stepped back, pushing him to the floor. He landed face-down, and I mounted his back. He was there for the taking. Interlocking my thumbs, I cradled his chin and cranked his neck up towards my chest. He grimaced. I was looking straight at Wendy and Mel. I already knew the look of Mel's arousal, but now I knew Wendy's. Another crank and he banged the floor with his hand. Mel swooned. I was the alpha male.

'Start counting!' I ordered Laura impatiently.

It was still early in the round and I knew I could finish it with two more quick submissions.

Kev was on one knee, rubbing the back of his neck. Laura gave him a slower count than she had given me and when she reached seven, he rose. I pounced, pushing him backwards with the force of my forearm. He toppled, hitting his head on the floor. Planting my backside on his face and facing his feet, I thudded rights into his stomach. My thighs chafed on his sandpaper stubble as his groans were muffled beneath me.

'Get off him! He gave!' shouted Laura.

I drove one more into his abdomen for good measure.

'Fucking well count then!'

'One! Two!' she complied.

'Oh fuck!' gasped Mel.

'Three! Four!'

Wendy stood up to get a better view, and perhaps to assess whether her first aid skills would be needed.

'Five! Six!'

Kevin rolled to his side and curled up, grimacing. I strutted around him, glancing at Wendy. She stared back, sultry and simmering.

'Seven! Eight!'

'Get the fuck up, Kev,' I taunted, waving my fist at him, willing him to rise so I could knock him down again.

'Nine! TEN!'

Laura turned away from the loser, disgusted at the sudden turnaround and his capitulation. I looked at my prize.

'You fucking brute,' she whispered, shaking her head and smiling.

Turning to her two housemates she raised my arm, just as I had once lifted hers.

'The WINNER!!!' she proclaimed,'...of ME!!!' and giggled.

Wendy and Mel applauded and whooped. I acknowledged them with a slight nod and a subdued smile that registered nothing more than satisfaction at a job well done.

I wanted them to sense my power, not my joy - and certainly not my sense of relief.

Partially recovered, Kev finally clambered to his feet and stuck out his hand in a gesture of reconciliation.

'You tough motherfucker,' he muttered submissively.

Wendy spontaneously hugged me but let go quickly, suddenly mindful of my near-nakedness and Laura's proximity.

'What he said,' she whispered, kissing my cheek and blushing.

As she stepped away, Laura had her eyes on me, chewing her fingers.

I had beaten Kev, and she was mine.

'Bye, girls,' Kev waved towards the bed stoically. 'I won't hang around.'

He knew the score. Mel and Wendy waved back their goodbyes.

'See ya,' said Laura peremptorily, briefly looking up.

She flashed her palm dismissively and returned to her whispered conversation. Her ruthlessness was part of her appeal. I nodded towards Kev in acknowledgement. We both recognised that I was now flavour of the month. I knew it wouldn't last, but I was determined to savour it.

As Kev departed the bedroom, still in speedos and t-shirt, I strode to the centre, marking my territory, seeing him off. As the only man in the room, I was the sole object of their attention again. I basked in it, affecting an air of detached nonchalance as I attempted to sear the scene into memory. I wondered what Rachel would think, and whether I would ever tell her.

They went back to whispering on the bed and a wave of self-consciousness floated over me. I put my t-shirt back on. As adrenalin slowly subsided, the ache in my side was starting to burn.

Mel came over.

'That was incredible,' she effused, 'Thank you so much for letting us watch. I wouldn't have missed it for the world.'

Clearly under orders to make a prompt exit, she reminded me to let her know if Rachel ever fancied a comeback – 'hairpulling and slapping and everything!' - and stretched out her hand. As I took it, she slipped me a piece of paper on which she had written her e-mail address. I gave her a short hug, pecking her on the cheek before she left. I wanted to see her blush one more time. She duly obliged and scampered from the room, smiling, no doubt hoping to get a word with the loser before he left.

'Hey Champ,' said Wendy, stepping forward and blessing me with an air-kiss. 'It was a blast. Now I know what a guy-fight is like up-close. I think I'm a fan. I'd better leave you to your prize. It would be cool if our paths were to cross again.'

We looked into each other's eyes and there was a mutual sadness. I pulled Wendy into a wordless bearhug and for a few seconds she clung on tightly.

'One final transfusion,' she whispered in my ear.

'I love your energy,' I whispered back.

She quickly turned away and nodded to Laura.

'Have fun.'

Wendy left without looking back at me. As she closed the door behind her, I felt a pang of emptiness.

Finally, here I was. Another wild fantasy about to be realised, and already dissatisfied because another had taken root. Alone with Rachel's nemesis, in the room where she had demonstrated her physical superiority over my girlfriend in the most decisive fashion, Laura's stare penetrated me.

'Her or me?'

She couldn't hide her jealousy.

'Come here,' I beckoned, intent clearly etched on my face. 'You won me, and now I've won you. You. Definitely you.'

Three weeks after her triumph, and in the very same room, Laura yielded to me as magnificently and beautifully as she had destroyed Rachel.

'Fuck, yes,' she sighed, and submitted herself to me.

CHAPTER 3: THE COMEBACK

Though I was wearing a polo shirt, Rachel noticed the finger-marks on my biceps. She pushed up the sleeve and saw they extended to my shoulders. Yellowed bruises dotted both arms where Kev had grabbed them. She looked at me in puzzlement.

'Where did they come from?'

I decided to come clean. Not about Laura, but about the fight with Kev.

We were in my garden the weekend after it had happened, enjoying the unseasonably warm weather. There were two coffees on the patio table. It was a rapprochement of sorts.

We had seen little of each other between her fight and mine. She had said she wanted time to herself, and it was difficult being around her, so it wasn't hard to put some distance between us. We had not spoken about her defeat to Laura. It was taboo, an elephant in the room. I have no recollection of ever discussing it with her in detail.

I cannot be certain, but it is possible, even likely, that Rachel and I had not slept in the same bed between her fight and this moment.

Before I tried to explain myself, I took off my shirt to show her the full extent of the bruising which had developed on the side of my body. They were merely yellowed blotches now, nothing like as severe and widespread as the marks Laura had left on her.

'What happened?' Rachel repeated in consternation.

'I had a fight with Kev.'

Her eyes widened in disbelief.

'You what?!'

I glossed over the details. It was enough for her to know that I had been back to their house, Laura's house to be more precise, and that he and I had 'had a straightener.' I neglected to mention Mel or Wendy.

'Why didn't you tell me?'

'I know you wouldn't have given your blessing. I needed to put things right and I didn't want you to have to go back there.'

Rachel gaped at me incredulously, rose from her chair and threw herself into my arms. We embraced tightly. It was the first display of affection she had shown me since the night we could not speak about. My chest was moist from her tears.

It was clear that she understood it to have been an act of chivalry rather than the betrayal it really was. In her mind, I had avenged her or, as one might have said in days of yore, 'defended her honour.' I played along with her self-deception, hating myself for it yet grateful for her apparent re-emergence from the winter that Laura had imposed.

'Was she there? Did she watch it?'

We both understood who 'she' was.

'Yes.'

'And did you win?'

It was almost an after-thought.

'Yes, of course I won. I knocked him out in front of her, in the very same room.'

'My hero!' she exclaimed.

She meant it. We kissed. I took her inside and led her to the bedroom. I was a prick. Wendy's unspoken confirmation - when she evaded my question the previous weekend - was not required. I was all too aware of it.

It's indelicate to write about, but it felt different with Rachel that Saturday than it had with Laura the weekend before. Both equally memorable, both equally satisfying, yet two completely different experiences.

With Laura, I needed to dominate. She was a victress; the sex was aggressive and passionate, rough, even bestial. I wanted her to quake under my power. Our mutual desire was palpable. But magnificent and validating though it was, sex with Laura was fuelled by a kind of raw, wild power. It was my first proper taste of that very rare thing: 'hot bitch sex,' as I came to call it. We needed to unleash ourselves on each other, but it felt like we burned ourselves out in the heat that we generated. Neither of us was under any illusion it could be sustained.

With Rachel, I felt the need to protect and nurture. She was still a fighter and I was both proud of, and grateful for, her re-emergence from defeat; re-experiencing sex with her was intimate, soulful, emotional. I felt she needed me in a way that Laura never could.

Rachel's body felt more superb than ever beneath mine. I recalled the moments in her fight when she had been the aggressor. I remembered her spirited trash-talk. I had seen something in her that night, something deeply impressive, that I had never noticed before, and now was the first occasion I had had to make love with her in awareness of this new aspect of her character. She moved her body proudly and without inhibition. Finally!

Rachel rediscovered herself in the following weeks, and our relationship was renewed. Spring had fully arrived. Her body language transformed, she re-intensified her fitness regime, she smiled again. I can't pretend that it was love – from my side, anyway - because ultimately it relied on my deception of her, but our mutual attraction and friendship returned.

We spoke about my win over Kev. She was interested to know how many submissions there were, how close the fight was, and how it finished.

'You're right. I couldn't have gone back there but now I wish I'd been there to see it. There's something so sexy about you knocking him out. I would love to have seen her face when you did it.'

I wasn't so sure about that.

I recounted how difficult it was to obtain submissions given our lack of technical proficiency, and that if he hadn't increased the level of aggression, we would probably still be there now, trying to get the best of seven.

'That's how it was between me and her, too,' Rachel said wistfully, thinking back.

She asked how Laura had behaved on my return visit, and what had been said.

'She was just kind of normal really. Don't you remember? She was actually alright during the first half of your match with her, before it all started getting a bit...'

I didn't know how to finish the sentence.

'Does she still hate me?'

'I don't think she ever hated you, Rachel. She's just a bit intense, that's all.'

We went on with our lives.

Spring had given way to summer. Rachel and I were lying in bed together on another Saturday morning, when it came out of the blue.

'Listen. You might not like this. I want to do it again. I want another catfight with her.'

I was horrified.

'What?'

'I've made up my mind. I want another catfight with her,' she repeated, looking at me in a way that left me in no doubt that she was serious.

I told Rachel it was crazy and that after pulling our relationship back to where it had been before, we didn't need to jeopardise it again.

'Don't you remember what she did to you?' I reminded her.

Laura's name was anathema.

'I need to do it for me, not you,' Rachel insisted.

It was – and still is – incomprehensible to me. Every atom of my being baulked at this terrible idea. I had visions of Rachel getting badly hurt again, but I was just as concerned that she would discover the full extent of my subterfuge.

'What happened to the guy who wanted to see me fight? You think I would lose again. Is that it? I won't. I promise. I'm in the best shape of my life right now and I would kick her ass. I know I would. I've been going to kickboxing classes, for God's sake! Let me prove it.'

Was this why she had been working out so hard for the last few months? It's true that her body had never looked better or more powerful. I asked where her desire came from.

'You felt you had to put it right. So do I. Until I beat her in a catfight, I'm always going to feel second-best. And you will always see me as someone who couldn't win a fight. I don't want to live with that.'

It made no sense to me.

'I'm always going to feel like Mike Tyson is better than me, because he fucking well is when it comes to fighting. It doesn't mean that I have to jump in the ring with him!'

She laughed.

'It's not the same. I don't want you to think of me as a loser, not even for one second. Do you have any idea how humiliating it was?'

I remembered her half-closed eyes after Laura had drained the spirit from them. I never discovered why Rachel's self-esteem was so fragile that she had to put herself at risk again. What kind of formative experience must it take to create a neurosis like this?

'Please don't,' I implored her, 'You're no loser. don't want her to hurt you again. You know what she was like last time. I'm not even sure she's 'all there'.'

Rachel said nothing for several minutes, her eyes on the ceiling as she contemplated my objections.

'I'll compromise,' she concluded. 'If you can find someone else, I'll catfight them instead. But if you can't, I will do it with her again – with or without you. I will. I need to win. I want you to see it. I even want other people to see it. It's crazy, but I just do.'

I said I would think about it.

Had I gone soft? Here was Rachel offering herself up to catfight for me again and I was about to reject it. The more I considered it, the more I realised that it was her choice of opponent which disconcerted me most. I only wanted to see her catfight again if it resulted in victory. Any other outcome was unthinkable, and I feared what Laura would do to Rachel if she were presented with another opportunity. Could I endure that again? Would I fall back under Laura's spell if she repeated her previous destruction? It would surely finish my relationship with Rachel and possibly send her back into a winter from which she might never emerge. Catfighting with Laura was like playing with fire. No, it was unconscionable.

And yet at the back of my mind, I also thought that if I could see Rachel win, just once, Laura would lose all relevance for me. I wanted to see Rachel prevail as much as she wanted it for herself. Perhaps Rachel sensed that. It didn't have to be Laura, though. If Rachel tasted winning, my God, what would that do for her self-confidence? How uninhibited might our lovemaking become if she could exorcise a neurosis which must have plagued her since who-knows-when? One decisive, significant victory would surely be enough. It would need careful planning and there was no room for error, but maybe it wasn't completely impossible.

Inevitably, my thoughts turned to Mel. She was ready, willing, available and most importantly in my estimation, beatable. But it wasn't that straightforward.

Aside from Mel's suitability as an opponent, there was the question of venue. The upstairs space in the house where Mel lived was an ideal arena for a catfight, but it had three considerable drawbacks.

Firstly, it was a den of bad memories, for Rachel anyway. The angel on my shoulder said that going back into the scene of the original carnage might fuck Rachel up and wreck her chances before a catfight could even begin. The demon on the other replied that if, or rather when, Rachel won, those memories could be expunged forever.

Secondly, Laura would be there, no doubt. It was her bedroom, after all. That would also get to Rachel, whispered the angel persuasively. Then again, retorted the demon, perhaps it could provide her with added motivation. Last time, Laura was able to draw out a side of Rachel that I had not recognised, and maybe her mere presence as a non-combatant would bring it out again. I knew Laura was a loose cannon, though. She had told me she wouldn't tell Rachel about what happened between us, but could I trust her? I imagined the delight she might take from exposing my infidelity and showing me up for the prick that I was. 'You owe it to Rachel to put yourself in that jeopardy,' whispered the demon, 'Stop thinking about yourself.'

My third concern about the venue was that Mel also shared the house with Wendy, who was still a frequent visitor to my thoughts. If I were to see Wendy again, I was afraid it might shake the very foundations on which I had started to rebuild my relationship with Rachel. The demon said no, a Rachel victory would also render Wendy insignificant. It was nothing, a temporary crush, and Rachel's inevitable victory over Mel would surely sweep it away.

Alternative venues didn't bear scrutiny. Fighting outside was inconceivable - we needed privacy. My small house with its tiny bedrooms didn't have sufficient space and Rachel rented with housemates - teacher-colleagues at school - from whom she would certainly want to keep this secret.

Ultimately, I concluded that the drawbacks of going back to the scene of the first fight might not be insurmountable if they could be properly managed.

But what about Mel as a prospective opponent? First, how confident could I be that Rachel could take her? I knew nothing of Mel's potential other than her own self-assessment of being an inferior wrestler to Laura and Wendy. I was familiar with Mel's physique, of course. I didn't think she could match Rachel's level of fitness. She was lovely, but also naïve and emotional. I recalled how she struggled to conceal both her horror and arousal at the two fights she had observed, and surmised that Mel might not last long when the going got tough.

It would be disingenuous for me to pretend that I wasn't very turned-on by the idea of seeing Mel and her glorious breasts doing battle against Rachel. In my fantasies they were topless, but there was no chance of Rachel agreeing to that. Every time I ran the fantasy over in my mind, though, Rachel came out on top. I couldn't see how Mel would beat her, but that raised another issue.

I had developed a degree of affection for Mel. She had sex appeal for sure, but I wasn't captivated by it in the way that I was by her two other housemates. Nevertheless, she was pleasant and puppy-like, energetic and eager to please. Though I would obviously want Rachel to win, I didn't want Mel's first catfight experience to be as traumatic as Rachel's. If Rachel fought again, would she feel the need to win in the same devastating manner that Laura had? I couldn't put Mel through that, could I?

The ideal would be a match sufficiently competitive for Mel to hold her head high at the end, yet sufficiently decisive for Rachel to emerge as the clear winner. Above all, they would begin and end on good terms, even as friends, with no injuries sustained by either party.

Can such a catfight ever be engineered, or does the emotional aspect of this female combat variant make it inherently unpredictable? Was Mel's enthusiasm to graduate from wrestling her housemates to catfighting Rachel an indication that she wanted something more violent and unpredictable? It didn't square with what I thought I knew about her character. Mel was so under-the-radar that I had barely noticed her originally. But could I be sure that she wouldn't emerge as a bitch every bit as spiteful as Laura? Laura would surely encourage Mel to turn my dream of a managed catfight on its head if that was what was required for victory.

There were so many unanswered questions.

We were sunbathing in the park near my house, and I was silently admiring the muscle tone Rachel had developed. I fantasised about her, dressed in those denim short-shorts and that mauve sleeveless top with the low hem-line, going up against Mel, attired in t-shirt and panties. If I couldn't see them fight topless, then bra-less might be almost as good. It was getting hot in the sunshine.

I couldn't shake the idea that catfights have an inbuilt emotional dynamic that can send them whirling out of control. Wrestling would be more manageable yet still generate most of the benefits that a catfight would. Mel might be persuadable.

'What if I could get you a wrestling match instead of a cat-fight?' I blurted.

I hadn't planned to say anything. It just came out. Rachel put down her book, looked at me, raised her eyebrows and smiled. Then to my - admittedly partial - disappoint-ment, she gazed into the distance and screwed up her nose.

'It wouldn't give me the same high.'

One traumatic loss on her record and now she was a cat-fight junkie.

'I want the emotion that goes with catfighting,' she ex-plained. 'That's what I enjoyed about last time. It's like I discovered a different person underneath that I didn't know existed, and she was cool. I liked her,' she said, temporarily referring to herself in the third person, 'Until I started getting my ass kicked. Even that wasn't so bad, until the very end. I don't blame you anymore. If I don't know when it started to feel more bad than good, why should I have expected you to?'

I wasn't going to let her exonerate me. I didn't deserve her forgiveness.

'Rach, I'm a prick and I should have stopped it. I was supposed to be looking out for you.'

'I wouldn't want you to have stopped it if I was doing to her what she was doing to me. I hated her - still do, actually - and it was energising. I know you think I'm nice but there's more to me, and it needs to come out sometimes. Next time, I want to be the one dishing it out and I want you to see me doing it.'

'Rach! You got hurt!'

'She didn't put me in hospital. I mended. What's that thing you say? 'What doesn't kill you, makes you stronger'.'

She flexed her biceps. They were small but solid. She was turning into a fucking Übermädchen, right in front of me.

'You know what it's like with wrestling,' she continued, trying to rationalise her need for the extreme. 'It might go all night without any submissions. Anyway, have you got someone in mind?'

She looked at me, expectantly. I was reluctant to say because I knew there would be no going back, but she knew me too well to hide it from her.

'You have! Who is she?!!!!'

I teased her, about to say the name several times, then hesitating.

'Tell me!'

She slapped my arm and I experienced a taste of what her future opponent might be in for. I gave in.

'Mel.'

No flicker of recognition.

'Do I know her?' Rachel looked puzzled.

Mel had clearly made the same featherlight impression on her as she had on me during that first encounter.

'Oh, wow!' she enthused, extending the final syllable when I reminded her who Mel was, and explained how she had made her interest known.

'She actually challenged me?! Why?'

She was both turned-on and affronted by Mel's temerity.

'Because she saw what Laura did and she thinks she can beat you,' I replied, conscious I was stirring a pot that really did not need stirring.

'Fuck that bitch,' Rachel sounded annoyed. 'Why didn't you tell me before?'

'It would mean going back there, and I'm still not sure that's such a good idea.'

The penny dropped.

'Would she be there?'

She meant Laura, of course.

'Probably.'

'If I'm going to go there, why don't I just fight 'her' then?'

'Because you promised me that if I could find you some- one else, you wouldn't.'

Rachel was on her feet, pacing, excited. It was reminis- cent of those few moments when she had Laura under pressure. I wondered how common it was for women to have a hellcat lurking inside of them, or whether I just happened to have unbelievable luck in knowing the few that did.

'Who the fuck does she think she is? I don't even remember what she looks like, but I want this. I really, really want this!'

She nodded to herself.

'Fuck, I want this!' she reiterated.

I said there was a lot of talking to be done first, and that was even before we could approach Mel.

'Let's talk about it afterwards,' she said.

'After what?'

'Get your stuff together. Take me back to your place. I need you to fuck me.'

Rachel had not been this sexually voracious in the nine months I had known her. Our lovemaking didn't reach the heights of the 'hot bitch sex' that I'd experienced with Laura, but it was close and it was sustainable. We'd have sex; we'd sleep; she would wake up thinking about Mel; we'd talk about Mel; fantasise about how Rachel would beat her; and then we'd have sex again. Rachel was turned on virtually all the time, and so was I. We hadn't even contacted Mel yet to accept her three-month-old challenge.

'When are you going to talk to her? I want this to happen soon. It's killing me!'

She was like a six-year-old waiting for Christmas. I told her about my fear of another catfight spiralling out of control, and that I wanted to plan things so that we got something as close to my imagined ideal as possible. She was amenable but insistent that any catfight would be an emotional affair. Risk and pain and the possibility of humiliation and the prospect of glory were what she wanted, she insisted, if not quite in those words.

I suggested we meet Mel before the fight to sort out ground-rules and break the ice. She agreed on condition that she didn't have to make friends with her before the fight. Afterwards, maybe. I remembered how Mel couldn't catfight her housemates because of her friendship with them and understood.

We did another photoshoot. Rachel, dressed as she had been in the park, held up a handwritten sign which read:

'Challenge accepted. Let's talk about it!'

My phone number was written on it. We sent the picture to the e-mail address that I had carefully kept, with no accompanying message.

We didn't have to wait long. Twenty minutes later, the telephone rang and we looked at each other.

'You answer it. It's your phone!' squealed Rachel.

I picked up. Mel's voice betrayed nervous excitement.

'Of course I'm still up for it!' she said breathlessly. 'I've been thinking about it for months!'

I told Mel that Rachel wanted to have a word. Rachel waved her hands, but I held out the phone and she eventually took it. It was hilarious to listen to their awkward conversation, even though I could only hear one side of it. Two young women, both desperate to fight each other, were trying to have a civil conversation.

'Yes, I'm okay. You?... Yes, I am serious, really... Much better... No, it was my idea... I told him before he even mentioned you... Yeah, it will, but I'm looking forward ...

I'm not worried about that... What are you thinking of wearing? ... For a while really...As as rough as you want to make it... Cool... I'm gonna hand you back now, OK?'

She passed the phone back to me, mouthing 'you pig!' when she saw my silent laughter.

I asked Mel to keep our plans secret from Laura for the time being, just until we'd had the chance to iron out the details.

'Oh, it's a bit late for that,' she said, and I realised that Laura was almost certainly listening next to her.

'Okay, listen,' I said, 'Call me when Laura's not there. We need to manage this carefully. I don't have a problem with her watching it, if that's what you want, but I don't want it finishing like, you know, last time. Tell Laura I need to speak with her as well, privately.'

Rachel looked confused.

'Okay.' Mel sounded pleased, 'This is going to be epic. Thanks so much for getting back to me. I'm not going to sleep tonight!'

I could not let Rachel be in the same room as Laura without speaking to Laura first. As it was, she e-mailed me. I got hard just from seeing her name in my Inbox.

'Hey you brute! We need to talk. Not on the phone. Come tomorrow night, say 7-ish.'

Rachel tended not to stay over very much during the week, so Wednesday evening saw me headed eastwards on the motorway.

When I arrived, Laura was waiting at the door, wearing a

light summer skirt over that black leotard. In retrospect, it was intentional.

'Welcome back, you beast,' she said, grinning.

Her skin was bronzed and her long dark hair was wet. It was the first time we had seen, or even spoken with, each other since the unforgettable day of our magnificent fuck three long months ago. It was awkward. Not knowing how to greet her, I gave her a brief hug and felt her breasts brush against my chest. If I thought her spell over me had been broken, I realised I had been fooling myself. That leotard was a constant reminder of her supremacy over Rachel. She took me through to the kitchen and caught me trying to detect other signs of life in the house.

'It's just us. Wendy's away with her quartet and Mel's out on a girl's night.'

It was an early warning sign. I had hoped to use the evening to talk privately (and separately) with Mel and Laura about how we might manage the catfight with Rachel. I also wondered if I might see Wendy again. Laura poured two glasses of white wine and handed one to me.

'I hear she's finally recovered then. Took a while.'

She smirked and waited for a response. I shrugged.

'You're afraid to let her fight me again, aren't you?'

She pierced me with her stare.

'We both know what you would do to her,' I admitted.

She enjoyed my acknowledgement of her superiority and nodded contentedly.

'Yeah, I would. Please let me.'

She gazed at me, perhaps planning how she would mutilate Rachel in a rematch. I was weakening.

'Where's she going to fight Mel?' asked Laura.

'How would you feel if we used the same room?'

She looked surprised.

'My bedroom?' she laughed, 'I take it that's my official invitation to watch? You've never seen it, have you, looking normal? Bring your wine with you. Come.'

I followed her up the stairs and into that magical space. There was a duvet on the bed. No duvets on the floor. Books on calculus and statistics were piled on a desk, in the corner which had previously served as Rachel's and my interval refuge. Three beanbags were neatly arranged in an L-formation in the neutral corner where Laura had beaten her senseless.

She took the glass out of my hand and put it on the table. Taking the straps of her leotard, I slid them off her shoulders and down her arms. My lips tingled on first contact with hers. We couldn't stop ourselves. The second taste of hot bitch sex was every bit as good as the first. We hadn't burned out.

We lay on the bed, basking in another afterglow. Laura's hand was on my chest, and I should have been racked with guilt, but I wasn't. It was as if I was living two separate lives. There was the 'me' who enjoyed being with Rachel, and a different, darker 'me' who was turned on by Laura simply because of what she had done to her, and how ruthlessly she had done it. For the first hour that I had known her, Laura had merely been attractive. Her dispatch of Rachel had made her totally irresistible. I reminded myself I was a hapless victim of the evolutionary principle.

'Are we done yet? Is it time to talk about Mel?' Laura asked, grinning like an imp.

'I get hard every time I think about you knocking Rachel out,' I confessed.

She pulled up the sheet and looked down at the evidence.

'You've been thinking about it a lot since you got here, then, haven't you?'

She raised her eyebrows suggestively, then bit her lip.

'Every time I think about you laying out Kev, I end up having to change my panties. I've done a lot of laundry lately.'

We kissed and she broke off, looking serious. That stare again.

'I want you to be the first.'

I didn't understand.

'No condom. I have other protection. Come inside me. I want to feel your heat.'

Half an hour after burning together, we burned again. This time was slower, more sensual. From all fours, she slid herself back onto me as if her eggs were as desperate for my sperm, as my sperm were for her eggs. She rose to her knees and my hands cupped her breast from behind, coaxing her bum back towards me. This time we kissed more tenderly. I kissed her neck, then her lips. The kissing was integral to the fucking. Her moans grew loud and she lost control. Being inside Laura felt complete, and my seed was rampant. Rachel had started to become Laura, and now Laura was becoming Rachel. I had become two people, yet they had almost become one, no matter that they still hated each other.

◆ ◆ ◆

We were still in bed half an hour later. Her hand was again on my chest, the wine untouched.

'Shall we try again?' asked Laura.

'To talk about the fight or to fuck?'

We both laughed. It was more than just fucking, now.

'I really like you and I want you to know that.' she said. 'You don't have to worry about me telling Rachel about any of this. I couldn't give a flying fuck about her, but I would never do that to you. Trust me.'

It was the first time I could recall her using Rachel's name, albeit closely followed by the F word. In doing so, I detected a sliver of Laura's humanity and became even more confused and attracted by her.

'I'm not jealous,' she continued, 'You and I were meant to fuck each other senseless, even if we were never meant to be together.'

'Laura,' I loved saying her name, 'You amaze me every time I see you, you know that?'

She did. She smiled back.

'Are you still with Kev?' I asked.

'I still see him. I see a few people.'

Wild girls need wild sex lives. She thrilled me and she killed me.

'Fucking winners really does it for me, though,' she whispered, easing my disappointment.

We both knew why we were so weak in each other's presence. She made one more valiant attempt to change the subject.

'So why did you want to talk to me about Rachel fighting Mel? What is there to say?'

'I don't want it to end in that corner with one of them being knocked out.'

I pointed to the beanbags.

'This corner? The one over here?'

She smiled playfully, rose from the bed, extended her hand and pulled me over to it. We still weren't done. On the beanbags, she was at my mercy again. I grabbed her hair from behind and used it to pull her rounded buttocks back onto me. We fucked on the exact spot where she had knocked Rachel out cold. It was like desecrating a grave. We shook each other's world until her inner thighs ran moist from the overspill of our mingled fluids, saturated in the scent of our sex.

Three fucks with Laura had taken about the same amount of time, all told, as it had taken her to devastate Rachel. Madness it may have been, but it was a madness of the most delicious kind.

'Do you think if we put our clothes back on, we might have a better chance of getting this conversation started?' I suggested.

'Yeah, Mel will be back soon anyway.'

We washed and dressed and kissed. I shared her towel. On the way back to the kitchen, we stopped at the bottom of the stairs and kissed again. It was intense and prolonged. Laura had become my drug. The sound of the key in the door made us separate like teenagers caught in the act; it was implicitly understood that nothing of what had happened between us should be communicated to Mel.

As soon as she caught sight of me, Mel exclaimed,

'Oooh, it's the wrestler! I hope I'm not disturbing any-thing,' and giggled.

She was tipsy but cogent. Laura and I exchanged a guilty look, but she didn't appear to catch on. I adjusted my stance.

'I didn't know you were coming tonight?' she said, a hint of suspicion in her voice.

'Not three times, that's for sure,' said Laura.

Mel looked puzzled.

'Well, I was in the area and thought I'd look in on the off-chance,' I blathered. 'Looks like I timed it well. Can I have a word with Laura first? Then you and I can have a chat.'

Mel went into the kitchen to make tea, and Laura showed me into the lounge. It was a cosy room at the front of the house, complete with a battered three-piece-suite, coffee table and a TV.

'Laura, I wanted to talk to you,' I said, adopting a more earnest tone, 'because I'm serious about not wanting it to be like last time. It will be difficult for Rachel to come back here. Just being in the same room as you will make her nervous.'

Laura smiled and her eyes glinted.

'Nervous or scared?'

'She actually wants a rematch with you,' I said, slyly.

'Does she now?' exclaimed Laura, delighted.

She licked her lips.

'The thing is, if she doesn't have a good experience this time, there won't be a rematch.'

I had no intention of there ever being a rematch, but it was good leverage for securing Laura's co-operation if she was soon to be in the same room as Rachel.

'What you mean is, you want me to behave myself.'

'If that's possible.'

'Trust me,' she assured me, 'I'll surprise you.'

I asked if she could meet Rachel somewhere neutral, maybe a few days before the match with Mel, just to clear the air.

'I'll play nice if you're there too. Best behaviour, promise, especially if it means I get to fight her again.'

I was concerned that things might boil over if she was too vocal in her support of Mel during the fight.

'Don't worry. I'll just sit on the bed like a good little girl,' she remarked, sweetly but sarcastically. 'Kev can be in her corner if you won't let me. He wouldn't turn down the chance to see another fight, especially if 'Rach the Flake' is involved.' she laughed. 'He fancies her. He won't be quite so pleased to see you though,' she added as an afterthought.

Who did she think would win?

'Depends how much I took out of her,' Laura speculated with her trademark smirk. 'Mel's better than you think - and she thinks you're hot so that will give her extra incentive. She knows you get turned on by it.'

'Will Wendy be there?'

I tried to sound matter of fact, even though my crush on

her had not abated.

'Of course. We both know she's into you, and she wants to size up that pathetic little bitch of yours. Wild horses wouldn't keep her away.'

'It's all a bit awkward, isn't it?' Laura continued, philosophically. 'Wendy and your loser-girlfriend are loved-up with you, and me and Mel just want to fuck you. Must be nice to be wanted.'

'I think you know how that feels,' I replied.

Empathy was not Laura's strongest suit, so I didn't take her comments about the others too seriously.

'What about you?' she asked.

'I just want to fuck you too,' I said, not completely convincing myself that it was sufficient for me anymore, and then added, 'It's just a shame that someone as respectable as me could never be seen in public with someone as wild as you.'

Her jaw dropped. I winked and she punched my shoulder. Laura was not your 'normal' girl, but apart from wanting to fuck her brains out, I liked her more and more just for being Laura.

'Fuck you, too,' she said.

We looked at each other and smiled. I loved her, in a way.

Mel entered, with two cups of tea.

'Your turn,' Laura said to Mel, 'I'm off to bed. You two can fix some dates. Don't seduce him tonight, though. I've worn him out already.'

Mel thought she was joking. I stood up and gave Laura a brief but affectionate hug.

'Remember not to kiss or hug me in front of Rach,' I

whispered.

She smirked and was gone.

'I'm confused,' said Mel. 'Are you back with your girl-friend or not?'

I told her that Laura and I were just friends now; that Rachel and I were back together; and that I would really appreciate if she didn't mention my previous indiscretion with her housemate. She shrugged. I imagined her in the opposing corner. For the first time, I was im-pressed, turned-on even, by the sight of those breasts that stretched the cotton of her t-shirt. She raised her eye-brows, aware that my thoughts were not entirely pure.

'I'm sorry. I was just trying to imagine you as a catfighter,' I blustered. My life was complicated enough. 'How are you feeling about it?'

I was expecting a deluge of words and emotion, but Mel's earnest expression was one I hadn't seen before. There was silence before she spoke. Maybe she was just tired from her night out. She paused between sentences, try-ing to find the right words.

'I know you like Rachel. I'll be friendly when I meet her, but at the fight it will be different. It is a proper fight after all, isn't it? You'll have to be okay with that – with me trying to hurt her. It's nothing personal. I don't hate her like Laura does but it's not a catfight if someone doesn't get hurt, and I will do everything I can to make sure it's not me.'

The look on Mel's face told me she was not expecting to lose.

'When it's over, we can be friends if she wants.' she added.

We discussed dates, and I said I would confirm with Rachel. When I asked Mel why she was doing it, I was genuinely curious. There was no man to impress, as far as I knew. There was no money to be won.

'I think I just need some attention,' she said.

There was no trace of sadness or self-pity, but I had the impression that Mel was used to being over-shadowed despite her obvious charms. I liked her a lot. Aware it was late, I rose and reached out my arms to her. She stood up and accepted my embrace.

'I think you are a very, very cool young woman.' I said with sincerity.

'You might not be so keen on me afterwards - unless you want to be the prize, of course....'

She looked me in the eye and waited for a response. I didn't know whether it was the alcohol talking or whether she meant it. We saw a flicker of requited desire in each other's eyes, but sanity just about prevailed.

'That would be cool. You'd probably have to beat up Rachel and Laura on the same night, though, and if you did that, I would almost certainly have to marry you.'

She smiled at the thought.

'Laura wouldn't have a problem with it.'

She maintained the eye-contact and I felt her intent.

My head reeled in the early hours on the motorway. My heart wanted Rachel; my soul wanted Wendy; my body belonged to Laura. And now Mel was literally busting into my thoughts.

CHAPTER 4: COOL BRITANNIA

It was the summer of Cool Britannia and a wave of optimism was sweeping the nation. Hot on the heels of a valiant defeat as the host nation of a football tournament the year before, the country was undergoing a revival. A New Labour government had recently swept to power, overturning eighteen years of Conservative rule. It was as if an entire nation had drawn a collective sigh of relief, oblivious to how deep the subsequent disillusion would become, and how rapidly the country was about to change, almost beyond recognition. I was too young to remember the tail-end of the Swinging Sixties, but this was its nascent Internet-age equivalent. The shackles were off, the holidays were imminent, and the sun was out. That summer was a last hurrah, although we didn't know it.

Rachel and I sat in the July sunshine at a picnic table in Runnymede Pleasure Grounds. We were starting to have second thoughts, and I was feeling guilty because it had been my idea.

'This just feels weird,' said Rachel, speaking for both of us.

The appointed hour came and went, and we were half-hoping that we might be excused the excruciating encounter that I had lined up for us. Maybe Laura had got cold feet. Mobile phones were still in their infancy, and I certainly didn't have one, so she had no way of contacting us. We waited, expectant and nervous.

A quarter of an hour after our arranged time, Laura breezed round the corner, waved and smiled broadly. She wore sunglasses, a white crop-top and navy patterned short-shorts. There were bangles on her wrists. It was the attire of many a red-blooded male's catfight fantasies. Not exactly subtle, I thought.

'Hey guys, so sorry I'm late,' she said without explanation.

We stood to greet her and despite my request from a few days before, she bowled into us with air-kisses, first me, then Rachel. A war broke out inside me and I sat down quickly, sneaking glances at her bare midriff. She was as arousing as ever, and I had to hide her inevitable effect on me.

'Let me make it up to you guys by getting you an ice cream,' she offered, but we both politely declined.

She sat down on the other side of the table. It had been nearly six months since her encounter with Rachel. This was a different Laura, a distant relative to the pillager that had ravaged Rachel back in February. She looked at Rachel and asked her how she was. Rachel, equally stunned by Laura's conviviality, said she was feeling great. Laura looked Rachel over sceptically for a moment. Was she sizing her up again?

'You look better,' said Laura, with little enthusiasm in her voice. 'I keep forgetting that you're five years older than me.'

Was that a dig? Subtext was never my forte.

'So,' she continued, looking at me for rescue, 'What did you ask me here to talk about?'

She had run out of small talk already. I explained to Laura what she already knew - that I wanted Rachel to meet her before the catfight with Mel on Friday so that any lingering awkwardness from February could be put to bed. Laura's eyebrows rose slyly when she heard the word 'bed' and I immediately regretted it. Pleasantries evidently over, the real conversation began somewhat awkwardly. Who could blame them for their discomfort? They had history.

Rachel tried to start. 'I wanted to thank you for letting us use your room on Friday. You didn't have to do that, and I appreciate it, especially after... you know.'

'Not a problem,' said Laura perfunctorily. 'It means I get to watch Mel and you in action. Maybe we will have a rematch someday, do you think?'

That was not the direction in which I wanted her to steer this conversation. I frowned. She noticed.

'You have no idea how much I would like that,' smiled Rachel, through gritted teeth.

Laura stared back at her with a hint of hostility, wordlessly accepting the implied challenge. Suddenly there was a tension in the air again.

'Hey, you gave me a good fight and you've got a decent chance against Mel,' replied Laura, with unintentional condescension.

She wanted to ramp up the tension even more but had noted my anxiety and was trying to conform, bless her. She desperately groped for the right words.

'I didn't feel awkward after our fight. Because I won, I guess, but I literally didn't give it another thought. I don't have a problem with you. We're cool with each other, yah?'

I hoped Laura's disingenuity was less obvious to Rachel than it was to me. I knew she still hated Rachel and that she was desperate to wreck her again in front of me. Rachel looked into the eyes which had watched her collapse from close-quarters.

'We were pretty aggressive. Maybe it went too far.'

Laura shrugged.

'Hey, it was a fight. You can't make an omelette without smashing a few eggs. You didn't get injured though, did you?'

It was more a freedom of information request than a genuine enquiry about Rachel's health.

'It took me a while but I'm over it,' said Rachel. 'It was a baptism of fire, and I came through.'

Laura raised her eyebrows, under obligation not to express herself. I knew she didn't think so.

'I learned a lot,' Rachel continued, 'I got stronger, and I've improved. Now I'm looking forward to seeing what I can really do. Hopefully, I'll give a better account of myself on Friday. I'm excited you're going to be there. It gives me added motivation.'

Laura nodded, looking unconvinced and somewhat put-out at Rachel's confident assessment of her recovery.

'We'll see, I guess. Mel's my friend though. I hope you're okay with me supporting her. I'll try not to make too much noise. They tell me I'm a bit of a screamer, so apologies in advance if I do. Nothing personal.'

As if to signal that she was finding it difficult to maintain her gargantuan effort, Laura turned to me and said,

'Anyway, I haven't seen you for ages either. How have YOU been?'

It had only been a couple of weeks of course, but Rachel didn't know that. I told her that life was busy and that I was juggling a lot of balls in the air. I didn't have to tell her that she was one of them. She already knew.

'Well, I hope they don't all come crashing down on you at once. You look fit, anyway. I guess someone is keeping you on your toes.'

We both knew who she meant.

'It's nearly your summer holidays, isn't it? We finished weeks ago. Most uni students go back home but we're renting the house again next year, so we thought we'd stay put for most of the summer. You haven't met Wendy yet, have you?' Laura looked at both of us, starting to have fun. 'She knows all about you and is so looking forward to meeting you both!'

'Oh, she wasn't there for the fight with Kev, then?' asked Rachel, I think innocently.

Laura lost her mental footing for a second and glanced at me for help. I gave the slightest shake of my head.

'Oh, I didn't even know you knew about that,' said Laura. 'He,' she pointed to me, 'said that you wouldn't want to know about it. Sorry, I didn't know how much I was supposed to tell. Wendy wasn't there, no. I can't remember where she was. It was just me and the unfortunate Kev.'

The unfortunate Kev.

'I forget, was Mel there?' Laura asked me, desperately trying to get her story straight.

'Yes, of course she was,' I reminded her. 'That's when she passed on the challenge to Rach.'

I hoped Rachel wasn't picking up on all the hesitations and contradictions in our account.

Laura looked over our shoulders, willing Mel to appear and put her out of her misery. It was too much for her.

'So, just between us,' asked Rachel. 'What was it like when, you know, he and Kev...'

Laura went to say something, then stopped herself.

'Well, it was, er, it was.... it was pretty hot, to be perfectly honest with you.'

The imp grinned at me and desire flashed across her face.

'He told me he knocked Kev out. Is that true?' asked Rachel.

Laura relaxed. She was on safer ground now.

'Yes, another knockout, believe it or not. I had to count the wet-wipe out myself,' she said unsympathetically. 'It was a let-down really. He,' she pointed to me again, 'was a bit of a brute, especially when it ended up on the bed. He just kept pounding away. I thought it was never going to stop.'

She was such a bitch.

'Wen... oh, never mind.'

She tried to suppress a smile.

'Wendy...?' encouraged Rachel.

'She said she wished she'd been there for it, that's all. She doesn't like Kev much.'

Laura was getting quite good at this.

'How did you feel about it?'

'Sad, I suppose?' replied Laura, looking confused and lying terribly. 'Oh, thank God, there's Mel!'

She jumped to her feet.

'I'm sorry it's been a bit quick, but I've got a lot to do, and you need to have a proper chat with her. I'll see you in a few days, okay? We'll open a bottle of white wine and have some fun.'

She winked at me and looked at Rachel.

'Not you, perhaps. You wouldn't last long against Mel if you were tipsy. We're good with each other now, though, yah?'

She scampered off with less effusiveness than she greeted us, casting a quick glance over to me as if to say, 'I've done my best,' and then high-fived Mel as they passed.

Mel didn't say anything or wave as she approached us. Her crop-top barely covered her ample breasts and displayed her midriff provocatively; the super-short tartan skirt, white knickers & knee-high white sock combo gave her that 'sexy schoolgirl' look. It suited her. Her shoulder-length hair was just perfect for pulling. Mel was hotter than she probably knew. If her facial features were unremarkable, her body was smoking.

'Wow,' gasped Rachel as Mel glided towards us, 'I only remember Winter Mel and her baggy jumper. I didn't realise she had that kind of body.'

Summer Mel looked like more than a handful. She held out her hand to Rachel first.

'Hi. Mel,' she said, re-introducing herself as if it might

have come as a surprise.

She probably spent a lot of her life re-introducing herself to people, I thought. With the passing of time, I still remember the voices of the women I saw fight, but not Mel's. Her timbre and accent are lost to me.

'Hi,' said Rachel.

She had three inches on her prospective opponent, but their different body-shapes made for an intriguing contrast. Both held back. Of course, they had met before, briefly and in passing, but now they were days away from fighting each other, just for the sake of seeing who would come out on top. One had experienced the suffering; the other had witnessed it. They both knew what lay ahead.

They looked at each other for a few seconds. Mel broke the silence and giggled.

'Well, this is odd.'

'Why did you challenge me to a catfight, Mel?' asked Rachel, straight out. 'When we first met, you didn't look like the type.'

'I think I just wanted a little bit more drama in my life,' said Mel happily. 'What's your excuse?'

'Same, I guess, plus I knew that this guy liked it.'

She gestured towards me. Mel looked at me and raised her eyebrows.

'When I saw you against Laura, I thought you were a bit like me. You were quiet at the beginning and then you came alive as it went on. And you were brave, too. I had my hands in front of my face when she beat you up at the end. Anyway, I said to myself that I had to toughen up a bit. We'd been wrestling around amongst ourselves for a few weeks and I was doing okay. It was fun, but not as exciting as that night between you and her. And I just thought, why not? Obviously, I can't properly catfight Laura because I have to live with her and anyway, she would probably beat me. I think it would be a lot closer between the two of us, no offence. I think I would have a decent chance against you.'

By the look on her face, Rachel had taken offence.

'You sound confident.'

Mel put her tongue on her upper lip, tilted her head and stared back at Rachel in a way that suggested she was.

'Okay. Is your boyfriend going to watch?'

'No. I don't have one at the moment. If I beat you, I might try and steal yours though,' she giggled.

'I wouldn't advise it,' said Rachel, testily.

She hadn't taken the comment in the humour with which I thought Mel had intended it. I stepped in and tried to guide the conversation back to its intended outcomes. We talked about dress; we agreed on a handwritten set of rules; they agreed that trash-talk would be acceptable up to the moment the fight ended, and not a second longer. It was civil and business-like, if not especially friendly.

'Maybe we'll be friends afterwards,' said Mel in non-committal fashion.

Reaching the end of our deliberations, she asked if she could have a private word with Rachel, and they wandered over to a tree, thirty metres or so away from me. They were deep in conversation and I wondered whether Mel was telling her about me and Laura, or maybe even Wendy. My concerns were not assuaged when Rachel came back, with Mel several steps behind. Whatever had been said had inflamed Rachel. I knew that look. The pursed lips, the forward stare, the rising colour in her cheeks. She was genuinely annoyed. I was confused.

'Is everything okay?' I asked.

'Yeah, it's fine. I think we're done for today,' replied Rachel curtly.

Mel lurked in the background, watching her carefully. She was smirking. What had Laura put her up to?

Rachel was pacing again. I wanted to get to the bottom of the tension between them before we went home.

'You girls look like you're ready to start the trash-talk now,' I remarked. 'You can both have one little nugget before Friday if you want. Keep it short though. Who wants to go first?'

Rachel did.

She walked back to Mel, fixed her with a glare and spoke in a menacing, low tone, nodding as she did so. I had rarely seen her so earnest.

'If that's how you want to play it, fine. You and me. Let's do it. Let's fucking well do it. You wouldn't believe how confident I am, little girl.'

It was completely out of character. I had only seen Rachel like that once before. Mel held her gaze without blinking, shook her head and laughed scornfully. She was completely unruffled.

'Don't cry, baby. Let's see if you can stay conscious this time. I'll send you pictures.'

They stared daggers at each other. I had no idea what was going on. If they had just agreed to do a 'work' and were acting out their parts, these girls deserved Oscars. Mel turned and looked me straight in the eye.

'I'll see you Friday. Get ready for something special. I'm going to give you a day to remember, and she's getting fucked up.'

She turned and walked back in the direction from which she had arrived, and I watched her backside slink beguilingly into the distance.

'What the fuck was that?' I asked Rachel.

She fumed, barely speaking, on the way home. I glanced across to her in the passenger seat. Her watery eyes were fixed straight ahead. She kept nodding to herself and clenching her jaw.

CHAPTER 5: CARNAGE

Rachel could barely sleep.

'This is it. This is really it,' she said when I opened my eyes and saw her face on the pillow next to me.

She had been grinding her teeth in her sleep, but now she was happy that the day had finally arrived. It felt right to spend the night before the fight together, so she had stayed over. We weren't supposed to get there until 1pm, so we whiled away the hours until heading eastwards. She spent the morning frustrated, tetchy, excited. Everything was building up.

We showered; we took a light breakfast; we made love; we showered again; we went for a short walk on another sunny July day. Rachel wanted to arrive in her fight-clothes, so she changed into the gear she had been wearing in the park that day, the mauve loose-fitting top and the denim shorts. She wore her hair up but would take it down when she arrived. She checked herself in the mirror. She took an extra outfit – not the electric blue leotard - just in case the mood called for it later, although it wouldn't be required.

With the fight against Laura, we had been stepping into

the unknown. This felt different. We knew what the room would look like. The frosty atmosphere had already been established. We knew the drill.

In the car, we listened to a Patricia Kaas album on cassette tape. Rachel had spent nearly a year living in France before I knew her, and we shared a niche interest in French pop ballads. I re-experience that journey whenever I listen to the same album today. *Quand j'ai peur de tout* seems, on the face of it, a title in direct contradiction to the situation Rachel faced, but the lyrics were somehow appropriate. Rachel was stepping back into the lion's den and I was proud of her. I told her so and she wiped away a couple of tears (as I do, even now, when I hear that track at a distance of twenty-four years). I'm still proud of her, if less proud of myself. Rachel recomposed herself. We stopped talking.

When we pulled into the road where they lived, I checked she was okay. We were both thinking back to that February night. Rachel looked back and nodded.

'You've got this.' I assured her.

We had hardly spoken on the journey. She had been so deep in thought.

Laura opened the front door. Kev waved from the kitchen without saying anything and I sensed Wendy was in there too even if she was out of sight. The knot in my stomach tightened.

'You know where it is,' Laura said, with only the most fleeting flicker of a smile. 'I suggest you go straight on up and we'll join you in ten.'

Everything felt heavy.

We climbed the stairs and walked past the closed door

of Mel's room. I was filled with conflicting thoughts and emotions. Laura's space had seen loss, victory, raw passion and betrayal. What more could it bring me? The desk and chair were gone; now the bed was covered by just a double sheet and two pillows; duvets re-covered the carpet; the beanbags were back in 'fight formation,' together with their attendant bottles. I glanced at the neutral corner and felt a sense of, almost, reverence. Rachel tossed off her shoes and socks, let down her hair and walked around the room, ending up instinctively in the corner which had been hers and mine.

'Show me where you knocked him out,' she said, and I did.

Rachel tried to imagine it. She took some deep breaths, performed a relaxation exercise and collected her thoughts.

Laura knocked on the door, checking it was okay for Kev and Wendy to come in.

'Alright mate?' nodded Kev and I walked across to shake his hand.

It was amicable. There was no hostility. We had left it all on the mat and there was nothing more to say.

'Thanks for the invite to watch this one. It should be an absolute belter.'

He walked over to Rachel and gave her a brief, polite embrace.

'You look great,' he said.

She really did.

'Thanks,' replied Rachel.

'You must be Wendy?' I ventured, to the fifth person in the room.

A smile played upon her beautiful face and her eyes widened.

'You're very perceptive,' she retorted, playing along, 'It's lovely to meet you at last. I've heard so much about you both. Is it true you're a wrestler? I hear you have an excellent coach.'

I introduced her to Rachel.

'Thank you so much for the opportunity to watch,' said Wendy to her. 'I've not seen a rules catfight before and I can't tell you how exciting it is.'

She seemed so genuine, and my crush for her came straight back, even with Rachel standing right next to me. I sneaked glances at the denim capri trousers which clung to Wendy's perfect form. Midriff-revealing crop-tops must have been in. Hers was navy. I savoured the sight of her lightly tanned lower back and marvelled at the auburn hair which washed over her shoulders as she wished Rachel good luck, 'but not too much'. It was clear where her loyalties lay.

Laura stood by the door, hugged by her own pedal-pushers and the white crop-top I remembered from the Pleasure Grounds. Kev and Wendy took their positions on the bed, and Rachel paced in her corner, trying to dissipate nervous energy. Laura beckoned in Mel. The audience of two greeted her entrance with whoops and a round of applause. She entered proudly, in the same skirt that she wore to the Pleasure Ground. Her shapely legs were bare, though, and I doubt she had ever looked hotter. For a moment, there was a calmness about her, but the smile vanished when she caught sight of Rachel.

The mutual hostility was palpable. Rachel stopped pacing and glared across the room contemptuously.

Whatever had been said at the park was still having its effect. We sensed the tension as they continued to eyeball each other in silence. Both pairs of eyes nursed unmistakeable malice and no-one but them could explain why – and neither of them chose to. No words, no smiles.

It seemed somehow inappropriate to go straight into the fight, and so we all savoured the pre-fight moment for a minute or two. Both fighters distracted themselves from each other – looking at their fingernails, taking a swig of water, stretching - and Mel looked across to Laura for moral support.

'Come on, Mel, now it's your turn to shine,' said Laura, pumping her fist next to her beautiful midriff.

Mel smiled and relaxed. She started talking to her friends. I can't remember what was said but it helped to ease some of her tension. I looked back into Rachel's eyes, wanting to be reassured by her confidence. She didn't disappoint me.

'Fuck, I can't wait to get my hands on this bitch,' she whispered to me, but I think the whole room heard it even if they pretended not to.

Unexpectedly and without ceremony, Mel removed her black crop-top, revealing her breasts in all their glory, and tossed it casually onto the beanbag behind her. She glanced at me to register my reaction and smiled suggestively. I swallowed hard – she was certainly making good on her promise of a day to remember. Then she glared back at Rachel. It wasn't in the script, but she knew what she was doing.

'Go girl!', said Wendy in support of her friend.

Rachel was my girl, obviously, but I didn't want either

of them to get hurt. The obvious depth of their shared antipathy unsettled me. I felt like a rider at the top of a sheer-drop rollercoaster: scared and turned-on at the same time. We had agreed that I would act as MC and ref, as well as cornerman for Rachel. Kev would do the honours for Mel. My 'managed catfight' dream had failed before it had started but I promised myself that, as their choice of referee, I would stop the fight before either one could get badly injured.

I invited them to the centre.

'Fuck her up, Mel!' urged Laura, unable to control herself any longer.

Mel strutted forward slowly, eyes fixed firmly on Rachel, in full awareness of her own sexual allure, intimidating; implicitly challenging Rachel to remove her own top. Rachel held firm. I asked them to shake hands. They simply glared at each other.

'Girls, you know why you're here,' I began.

Their eyes were locked on each other. Rachel's three-inch height advantage seemed bigger but Mel's smirk spoke volumes about her confidence. Both girls knew they were going to win this catfight, but only one of them could be right.

'These are the rules that both of you have agreed to. This is a best-of-five submissions catfight with a two-sub margin needed for victory. Rounds will last three minutes with breaks of five minutes. You may use wrestling holds; you may body-punch; you may direct slaps to face and body; you may kick and use knee-strikes. You may pull hair. BUT: No punches to the face; no joint locks; no biting or gouging; no choking; no attacks to genital regions. After a submission, you have ten seconds to be ready to resume the match or you will be counted out. Are you clear?'

'Yes,' said Rachel. She swallowed.

'Yes,' said Mel, snarling.

Neither broke the stare.

'Do you have anything to say, Rach?'

She clenched her teeth and gave a slight shake of her head, continuing to stare down Mel.

'Mel?'

Her headshake was accompanied by a slight curl of her lip. Their unexplained animosity was real and undiluted.

'Go back to your corners, girls, and get ready to fight.'

Unlike the match with Laura, there was no cheering from the bed. It was too intense. We were about to watch these girls scrap out their hatred.

Rachel, facing the wall, looked at the floor and did a fast-foot shuffle on the spot.

I checked with Kev, who was timekeeping, and declared 'Fight!'

Rachel turned, raced across the room and had her hands in Mel's hair before the shorter girl knew what was happening, yanking her straight to the floor. With Mel on hands and knees, her white knickers showing under the tartan mini-skirt, Rachel then planted a thudding kick into Mel's side which caused her to yell out in pain and sent her onto her back. It was a blistering start from my girl and already Mel knew she was in deep water.

Rachel could have straddled her at that point, but instead moved swiftly behind Mel's head, grabbed a handful of hair again and literally dragged her up off the floor with it, grunting with the exertion as she used the backwards momentum to hurl Mel into the plasterboard partition which separated this room from her own bedroom. Mel's breasts juddered as she hit the wall and she cried out, distressed and already hurt.

'How does that feel, bitch?' yelled Rachel.

A shocked Laura attempted to shout encouragement to her housemate, but Rachel had the bit between her teeth. Mel had lost her orientation and Rachel was on her, grabbing hair with both hands again, kneeing her midriff and slinging Mel to the floor a second time. Another kick to the side sent her sprawling and this time Rachel jumped on top. Mel's breasts became cushions and, yanking Mel's head to her crotch, Rachel rained in right-handed slaps to the body.

'Am I hurting you, huh?! Come on little girl, you can do better than this!'

Mel squealed beneath her. She was being overwhelmed.

The slaps were wild and hard. Beneath the tangle that her hair had already become, Mel screwed up her face but was too proud, or maybe too shocked, to submit. Rachel jumped up, pulled her up by her hair yet again and applied a front headlock. She caught my eye and smiled at me, enjoying exerting her dominance over her rival. She made sure everyone could see how in control she was. Mel's breasts dangled forlornly as she was marched back to the neutral corner, just as Kev had done to me. Rachel had perhaps planned this. The neutral corner, the place of her February nightmare, was about to become the corner of her redemption and Mel's unravelling.

Rachel had Mel exactly where she wanted her. She released the headlock and took a step back for leverage.

Mel looked up to get her bearings, no doubt wondering why Rachel had let her go. There was a moment of stillness. She was trapped in the corner. Both looked at each other. Rachel then hit Mel with a full-on face-slap that rocked her like the one that had once shocked Laura. Mel, stunned, took the shot well but it stung her and she covered up, afraid of what might come next. Rachel took a step back again. She feinted, as if to throw a punch to Mel's stomach and Mel dropped her hands. Rachel glared at her again and we knew it was coming. Mel must have known it too.

The second hard, hard slap to her left cheek sent her into the wall and Mel dropped to the floor in a sitting position against the corner wall. Realising the helplessness of her situation, she began to cry. Not just tears but unrestrained sobbing. Undeterred, Rachel stood over her, straddling her body, and unloaded a flurry of hard slaps to her face with both hands.

'Come on bitch! Fight back and stop crying. You're pathetic!' she screamed.

Laura went to move off the bed but Kev pulled her back.

Mel raised her hands to protect her face and Rachel stamped her heel heavily, once into the midriff and once into her breasts. Mel tried to slump but was held up by Rachel's legs and the slaps continued to rain in. I had seen enough. Without waiting for a submission, I dragged Rachel off. No count was needed. It was clear that this fight was over almost as soon as it had begun.

'YES!!!' shrieked Rachel in a moment of total catharsis, spinning away in delight.

'Fuck you,' whispered Laura under her breath, but Rachel didn't hear it.

She was healed.

Mel was a traumatised, sobbing heap and the room was in shock. The destruction had been short, brutal and absolute. It had probably taken about two minutes, three maximum.

I went to Rachel as she regained her breath, inspecting her floored victim from her own corner. Tears of relief began to roll down her own face. Elated, I hugged her, and she let me lift her off the ground. On landing, she draped her arms around my neck and sobbed.

'My God, Rach. You steam-rollered her. That was incredible. You absolute champion!' I whispered into her ear, and we held each other close in another prolonged embrace.

I turned around to see Kev, Wendy and Laura crouching down, trying to console the stunned Mel, who had her head in her hands, still shaking. Wendy was checking to see whether Rachel had left any lasting damage. Eventually satisfied, she helped Mel to her feet and walked her over to the bed where she sat her down, still crumpled and crying. Wendy held Mel's hand for comfort as Laura went off in search of Band Aids to cover the grazes on those parts of Mel's body which had been marked by the walls, floor, and Rachel during the blitzkrieg she had just endured. Kev nodded a quick congratulations to Rachel and left with Laura.

It was just the four of us. For a few moments there was a stillness, punctuated only by the sound of Mel's abating sobs. Rachel's demon left her. Becalmed, she went to Mel's corner, picked up the crop-top and brought it to her rival on the bed.

'Here you go, poppet.'

Wendy moved back and Rachel crouched down before Mel. In her eyes I saw a determination to show Mel the concern that Laura had once neglected to show her. She helped her pull the top over her breasts, then looking gently into her eyes, rubbed her hands slowly up and down the slouched arms and shoulders of the girl she had just beaten up.

'Mel, I'm sorry,' she said, 'I'm sorry it had to be like that. Are you okay?'

Mel nodded without speaking. They rose to their feet and silently embraced each other.

I made eye contact with Wendy. She was also in a state of shock. As the two former enemies consoled each other, she came over to where I was standing in Rachel's corner, the spot where our best conversations had once taken place. I held both my hands out to her and she took them. She sensed, I think, that I needed her energy again. Maybe she also needed mine. I asked her if she was okay. She said she was, but there were tears in her eyes.

'I wish we could have a proper conversation, but this isn't the time or the place,' she said quietly.

I pulled her towards me, and she briefly put her head on my shoulder. When they came back into the room with a box of Band Aids, it was a strange sight that must have greeted Laura and Kev.

Kev accompanied Mel back to her room. She walked past me, careful to avoid eye contact.

I was now alone in the room with the three women who I loved in ways so different that I was helpless to choose between them. I wanted to get Rachel home as soon as I could. Wendy sensed it. She sensed everything. She took Rachel's hands and pulled her into a quick embrace. Standing by the door, Laura watched.

'Remind me never to have an argument with you,' said Wendy before leaning forward and whispering something in Rachel's ear.

Rachel nodded, almost overwhelmed by Wendy's kindness; went to pick up her bag with the outfit that was never used and walked towards the door. Now it was my turn. I looked at Wendy, not knowing if it was for the last time, and pulled her into me again.

Uncomfortable in each other's close proximity, Laura and Rachel waited impatiently near the door. They hadn't yet spoken to each other. It had been much easier for them to be civil to each other in the neutral surroundings of the park, but this was the room where Laura had destroyed her. I was reluctant to let Wendy go. Our hug was just intimate enough that Rachel raised an eyebrow, but not so intimate that it raised her suspicion. Wendy whispered her AOL address in my ear and checked to make sure I had understood. I nodded, committing it to memory. It was so short and straightforward that I could tell you it now, all these years later.

Laura caved in, bit her top lip and tipped her head towards Rachel in grudging acknowledgment.

'Congrats. That wasn't bad. You jumped her at the start, though, and it wasn't very nice of you to carry on hitting her when she was already crying.'

Rachel's mouth dropped open. It was not as if Laura had been a stickler for ethics when there was a fight to be won. She fixed Laura with a stare.

'If you don't shut your fucking mouth, bitch, I'll shut it for you.'

Words on the page can't convey the incongruity of how it sounded when spoken in a soft, educated, female English accent. That was Rachel. She still had some adrenalin to burn. Laura couldn't help snorting her derision and abandoning the pretence of civility that she had managed to maintain until that point.

'Oh sure. Like last time I suppose, darling,' she said with heavy sarcasm, not taking her eyes off Rachel.

'No. Very different from last time. Very different.'

The contempt that had burned inside Rachel for Mel had transferred to Laura. I had seen enough for one afternoon and went to stand between them.

'I WILL fuck you up. Just give me a date, bitch,' demanded Rachel quietly, 'We can do it now if you want. Go and get changed. Let's get this done now.'

She looked straight into her eyes. Laura seemed moment-arily flustered.

'I've got some health issues. As soon as I've dealt with them, we will fight, come hell or high water, and I will knock you out cold again. You've forgotten who you are fucking with, you pathetic bottom-feeding haddock-clunged scum-weasel.'

Rachel couldn't help herself. She smiled broadly and laughed out loud at Laura's imaginative language, and Laura, seeing it, couldn't prevent herself from also burst-ing into a fit of unrestrained giggles. Before I knew it, they were both engulfed in a wave of mutual hilarity until they were literally weeping with mirth. The anger had completely dissipated. It was weird.

'Come here, you cheap skank,' said Rachel, sliding past me.

She grabbed Laura in an embrace. Judging by the face she pulled over Rachel's shoulder, Laura was stunned for the second time that afternoon. My brain was also struggling to process it, but I was rapidly getting used to living in a state of utter confusion. Rachel let go of Laura and smiled at her.

'I will fight you one day, and I will beat you, but I'll stick to the rules and maybe we'll be friends afterwards, no promises though. I'm not frightened of you and I like you in spite of what you did to me. I even admire you, in a way. We're good, yah?' she finished, imitating Laura's accent.

Laura shook her head, speechless, rooted to the spot in shock and confusion. Rachel headed for the stairs. I thanked the goddess of catfighting for somehow restoring order, temporarily at least.

'Are you okay, Laura?' I asked with some concern.

She hadn't mentioned any health problems to me before. She certainly looked well.

'Don't worry. I'm fine.'

I thought I saw her lower lip quiver, just slightly. Rachel was out of sight and half-way down the stairs, so I took the opportunity to hug Laura properly. My attention had been split at least four ways that afternoon and she hadn't received enough of it. She held on for a second or two longer than I was expecting, and I kissed her on the cheek as I left.

'Enjoy your fuck!' she called after me.

'Let's not talk until we get to your place,' said Rachel as soon as we got in the car.

She closed her eyes, and we listened to Patricia Kaas, and every time I glanced across to Rachel, a look of contentment adorned her face.

We reached home and went straight upstairs. I didn't want her to get showered. I wanted her body-sweat; I wanted her raw; I wanted her with Mel's DNA still on her skin; I wanted her straight away. Her lips and skin tasted salty. We tore each other's clothes off and went at it like animals. No words or foreplay. The sex was as aggressive and uncompromising as the fight had been, as much on her part as on mine. It was reminiscent of the 'hot-bitch sex' I had enjoyed with Laura, but it had its own character. Rachel had been sexually uninhibited in the last few weeks, but now she was off the scale. She rarely spoke when we made love, but now it all came out. Every time I thrust into her, it was another chance for her Shadow to exult in triumph.

'Did you see that big-titted cow, the way she looked at you? Did you see what I did to her? I fucking killed her! I fucking killed her right in front of you! How did that feel, huh? You didn't know I could do that, did you? I think I deserve you now. Give me my fucking prize! God, I completely tore that bitch apart! I was so nice to her at the end, but you know what? I was thinking that I wanted to do it again, and that I could do it to her again anytime I wanted. And fucking well leave her there so they could scrape her off the floor again. And I fucking well would as well! I want to do it again, and make her scream next time, not just cry. And make that fucking bitch beg me for mercy! Are you proud of me? How proud are you? Tell me! Tell me!'

Whether she was doing this for my benefit or hers, I could not honestly say. I can say, though, that it was the best sex she and I ever had. And I certainly told her that I was proud of her – in forthright terms. She revelled in her glory.

'And you know what was even better? When I called out that other bitch-faced cow! She's fucking scared of me now! Huh? You saw the look on her, didn't you? Health issues, ha! I would give her fucking health issues! She knows that I will fuck her up next time! Fuck her up so bad there will be nothing left of her! I'm going to wipe that smug look off her face for all-time! I know how much you want me now. I know how much better it feels for you to make love to a winner. I saw what was in your eyes when she beat me up the first time. I'm the queen now, though! You saw how scared she was! You know it and she knows it! When it happens, I will fucking murder her! I want to go back and do it tomorrow! How long do you think she would last against me, huh? I tell you, I will fuck her up SO bad! And you need to be there because if there's no-one to stop me, I swear I will fucking kill her. You want to see that, don't you, and I would love to give it to you! I would give you her fucking head on a plate! Show me how much you want me! Show me how much you want me to knock her out cold!'

I finished her from behind. As we both climaxed, Rachel threw herself face-down on the bed, and cried her eyes out. I rolled her over and she put her arms around my neck and continued to cry as hard as I had ever seen her cry. Gradually, her body quietened and stilled, as if all the excess energy and anxiety had finally taken leave of her body. She rested, exhausted, in my arms.

Half an hour later, in bed, as I ran my hand over her contours, she asked what I was thinking. I said that what was most incredible of all was that there wasn't a scratch on her body. For all of Mel's hard-talk in the build-up, Rachel had put her away without having to take a single shot. That it was the most one-sided girl-fight I had ever seen.

'You know why, don't you? You must know,' she said.

I told her, genuinely, that I didn't.

'We were fighting for you,' she whispered, and then burst into tears again.

Mel had told her in the park that she was going to knock Rachel out, and that when she did, I would only have eyes for her. She'd said that after Laura knocked Rachel out, I had become besotted with her (Laura). I don't think Mel gave away that Laura had been the prize for my fight with Kev. If she did, Rachel didn't let on. But in the park that day, Mel had said that it wasn't fair for me to have to fuck a loser like Rachel and that if Mel knocked her out, she should give me a 'free pass to spend a weekend' with her because I was going to be thinking about her anyway. From what Rachel was suggesting, Mel was pretty confident that a free pass weekend with her would be sufficiently thrilling that it would turn into something much more permanent. It had Laura's fingerprints all over it. She wanted to fuck me; she wasn't fussed about sharing me; and she was hellbent on breaking Rachel.

'So, I agreed that whoever won the fight, got you. I know it was stupid and crazy, but she got to me,' confessed Rachel.

Even after the fight, it was an arousing thought. Had I

known about their agreement beforehand, it would have driven me insane with desire.

'And was I going to get any say in this?' I asked, pretending to take offence, 'I'm just a piece of meat to you women, aren't I?'

'If she had done to me what I did to her this afternoon, could you honestly say that you wouldn't have taken the free pass?' asked Rachel. 'I wouldn't have blamed you. I would have wanted you to have her too because I was the one who agreed to it in the first place. Every time I imagined you making love to her, it made me want to kill her. I know how you guys are. I saw it in Kev's eyes too. When he congratulated me after the fight, I could see that he was dying to fuck me just because of what I'd done to her.'

I told Rachel that I would always choose her, no question. In my heart, though, a part of me suspected that if Mel had destroyed Rachel as comprehensively as Rachel had demolished her, I would have fallen for Mel and her glorious breasts in the same way that I had fallen for Laura and her glorious everything.

CHAPTER 6: ANCHISES AND APHRODITE

I almost had it all. I was having 'hot-bitch sex' with Laura and Rachel within days of each other. Mel had been so hot for me that she wanted to knock Rachel out just to have the chance of fucking me. Rachel was so hot for me that she wanted to kill all her rivals. And all that wasn't enough. I wanted Rachel. I wanted Laura. I had lost my interest in Mel. But more than anything, I wanted Wendy, and she was the most out of reach. She was too classy for me; too kind for me; too out-of-my-league.

Maybe she thought about me too, I told myself. She had told me her e-mail address, hadn't she? It was my only real means of contacting her. I could have telephoned the house that they shared, but how many times would it have been intercepted by Laura or Mel? So, within days of Rachel's triumph over Mel, I tilted vaingloriously and unfaithfully at the treble. My hubris was fast approaching its peak.

Dear Wendy

I think we should have that conversation. This weekend only,

I have access to a big, empty house in Bath and I can't think of anything I would rather do than spend some time with you there. Don't judge me. No pressure to do anything you don't want. I'll bring you back whenever you want. Just say yes or no in your reply. If it's yes, I'll pick you up outside your house at 6pm on Friday evening. If it's no, then I promise never to bother you again.

T.

I pressed 'send'. I hated myself for my continued deception of Rachel, but my heart beat fast at the thought that I might see Wendy again, and soon. For fifty-two hours I was virtually tied to my computer, unable to separate myself from my Inbox other than to sleep and eat just in case she deigned to reply.

Dear T.

Yes! It would be a delight.

W.

It was possibly the shortest, and certainly the best, e-mail I ever received.

My parents lived in Bath, in an Edwardian terrace house, but they had just left for a week's holiday in France, and I grasped the opportunity it afforded me.

Wendy was waiting at the corner of her road, so there would be less chance of Laura or Mel becoming aware of our tryst. She had told them that her string quartet was spending the weekend at a masterclass; my excuse to

Rachel was that I was meeting up with some old school-friends and wouldn't be back until late Sunday night. Rachel had some schoolwork to prepare even though we were in the middle of the holidays and, perhaps out of a sense of guilt, I said she could use my place over the weekend as it had a decent PC. She preferred working there as it was quieter than her shared house and she found it easier to concentrate.

'Throw your bag in the back and jump in the front,' I said, greeting Wendy.

She climbed in and smiled.

'Finally, alone together!' she exclaimed.

'There's so much I don't know about you, and I want to find out as much as I can this weekend,' I said.

'Likewise, Mr Mystery Man,' she replied. 'We might only have this weekend, so let's make the most of it. Thank you for whisking me away. I've always wanted to be whisked.'

I found it hard to believe that nobody had ever whisked her away before. I was in love with Rachel; in lust with Laura; and in total awe of Wendy. She was like a Renaissance painting come to life. I was driving with Aphrodite as my passenger, and I dreamed of being her Anchises. Wendy was by far the most beautiful woman I had ever - have ever - seen; and I was about to spend a weekend with her. I was a complete prick in terms of how I was treating Rachel, but I didn't care.

The M4 buzzed with Friday evening traffic, and we followed the big sun in the west. She told me that she hardly ever ventured outside Greater London and that she had never visited Bath. We shared our personal stories for most of the journey. As we snaked the winding road that leads from the motorway into the city, Wendy said,

'I'm glad we've got all the facts out of the way so quickly. I'm interested in what's left – who you really are.'

'Ah. So, you want to remove my mystique! What if there's nothing behind the curtain?'

'I know there is. I've peeked.'

There was a pause before she continued.

'Can we not talk about catfighting or Rachel or Laura until Sunday, though, please? I know we have to talk about it, sooner or later, but let's just have tonight and tomorrow together, first.'

That's exactly what we did, and I'm glad of it. I don't need to record the details here because it's tangential to the purpose of this account, and because there is no danger of me ever forgetting them in this lifetime. On Friday we shared our bodies and on Saturday we shared our souls. We talked about God and Beethoven; Ancient Greece, Israel, and Ireland; Sex and Love. It's all that needs to be said. If I could press pause on any moment of my life, just so that I could have the joy of living it forever, it would be 11pm that Saturday evening.

But Sunday came.

An air of sadness pervaded Sunday morning, because we knew reality was calling us back, and because the conversation that we had been putting off since we arrived needed to be had. We sat on a park bench on a hill overlooking the city and Wendy rested her head on my shoulder. I told her that this very spot had once been a favourite haunt of Jane Austen when she was a resident and had inspired a scene in her novel, Northanger Abbey. Wendy gazed wistfully through the clearing in the trees at the toytown below us and held my hand.

'Do you feel guilty?' she asked.

I nodded.

'I like Rachel,' she continued, 'I really warmed to her when I saw how she treated Mel after their fight. But she doesn't own you, and you don't own her. That's why I don't feel bad about this weekend. You haven't betrayed her, and I haven't done anything wrong either. We were free to get to know each other and I've enjoyed every second of it. I wanted to fuck you from the moment I saw you beat Kev so convincingly. I'm a free spirit, though. There are so many men and women in this world that I want to get to know. Exploring each other as we have this weekend has just been so joyful, hasn't it? I want my life to be like that. This weekend could not have been any more wonderful for me, but I must begin to pull away from you now because, if I get any closer, I'll feel trapped. And then I'll want to escape. And then the closer we are, the more it will hurt both of us. Do you see?'

She was at least seven years younger than I, but she sounded wise beyond her years. I nodded again, despite my incomprehension and sadness at what she had just said.

'I'm a lot like Laura in that sense,' she said, and then paused as she considered it. 'Isn't it crazy, how we both ended up here on this park bench, together, today? It must have been a one in a billion chance, but it happened.'

'And all because Laura and Rachel were looking for a fight with a stranger, and found each other,' I added.

'You know me better now. You were evasive the last time I asked you this, but I want to ask you again. Do I beat Rachel in a catfight? And what about Laura too?'

I did know her better. I had felt her physical strength and her passion that weekend, and it hadn't left me disappointed. She could match both in terms of agility, power and spirit. I told her so.

'That's cool. I'm so pleased to hear you think that. I know you'll fantasise about me catfighting both of them, if you haven't already,' (I had), 'so I just want to ask you a favour: please make sure that I end up winning at least half of those battles that take place in your imagination. I want you to think of me as a winner too.'

'I already think of you that way,' I assured her. 'Up until this weekend, you won about a half of those fantasy battles. Now you'll probably win almost all of them.'

'Only 'almost'?'

She smiled but she seemed content.

'I won't get to see you in action in real life then,' I ventured as my hopes of seeing Wendy catfight receded into the distance.

'Catfighting? No. No way. I wrestle Laura a fair bit, and I give as good as I get if you must know, even though I say so myself, but a catfight? No, I don't think so. I didn't know what to expect the other day. Don't get me wrong, it was fascinating and dramatic to watch and even thrilling, but I felt upset at the end of it. I don't think I could do that to anybody. Just as well probably, seeing as I'm training to become a doctor. It's not even because Laura is my friend. I wouldn't catfight with Rachel, or anyone for that matter.'

'Have you imagined it, though?'

She smiled and looked away, and we both knew that she had. We looked out over the city. She wondered how to communicate what else was on her mind. A minute or two passed.

'I don't know if you're aware,' she said, somewhat hesitantly, 'but Laura's grown too close to you, and now she's feeling trapped. Not by you, but by her own emotions, and it's hurting her. She thinks you're going to dump her because of what you saw Rachel do to Mel the other day. She thinks you don't need her anymore, and she's not coping well with it. Not well at all, actually. She doesn't let on, but I know her. And the only thing that will get her through it is if she dumps you before you dump her. If it's the other way round, she will be a wreck.'

It was only early August, but already my summer had started to reach its end. I desperately didn't want to let Laura go. The more I knew her, the more I liked her, but the only thing that bonded us, really, was the incomparable sex.

'So, what's stopping her?'

'Nothing is straightforward with Laura - you should know that by now. There's a repeating pattern thing going on with her, and I know how it's going to play out and, I'm her friend but, I think you need to know what's probably coming.'

I must have looked confused.

'She fancies a guy; has sex with him a few times; then falls in love. And then she gets scared of losing him. She can't handle that kind of emotion. So, she finds another guy, but that's not enough. She's never content with the next guy until she's seen him...,' she paused, waiting to see how well I understood Laura.

'Beat the first guy in a fight?'

She nodded.

'This will be number three. You against Kev was the first guy-fight, I've seen, but there was also one before which Kev won.'

It dawned on me that my destiny was to be a sacrificial lamb.

'She's found the next guy, hasn't she?' I asked, pre-empting what Wendy was about to say. She nodded. 'And?' I asked.

'Six foot two, 110kg. Plays American Football for the uni.'

'Have you seen him?'

She nodded.

'Hot?'

Reluctantly, she nodded again.

'There's not much point me even turning up, is there?'

'Your decision.' said Wendy. 'She can't force you, obviously. There's nothing in it for you. If you win, she'll just find someone even more intimidating for you to fight next. I suppose the only reason you could possibly have for doing it would be as a personal kindness to her, even though she wouldn't ever know it or see it as one.'

'A personal kindness?'

'Because if she doesn't see you lose to him, she'll never be certain that she found someone better and she'll always have some doubt. It would be a personal kindness to me too.'

I was confused again.

'Laura was attracted to you because she saw you win that fight against Kev. So was I. If you hadn't won, I would have thought you were a perfectly 'nice-enough' guy, but we wouldn't have spent this weekend together. You won a fight, and it turned me on. It's not just a me-and-Laura thing. All women are attracted to winners; it's biology. And it's not just women. Look what happened to you when you saw what Laura did to Rachel.'

I could hardly deny it.

'If recent history is anything to go by,' she continued, 'you'll get a call from Laura soon. I know the sensible thing would be to tell her to fuck off, but if you decide to go through with it, I'll be your sponge-lady, or whatever you call it. Seeing you lose will make you a little bit less hot in my eyes and Laura's, but it might be the best thing for all of us. I would still care about you, I really would.'

I was stunned. The leaves were already falling.

'Just one other thing. If you're brave enough to go ahead with it, I suggest you don't tell Rachel, and certainly don't let her watch.'

I thought about it.

'I need to ask you a personal favour now: if I take the fight and lose, can you at least promise me that I'll win at least half of the guy-fights that take place in your fantasies? It's important to me that you still think of me as a winner.'

'Hey, I saw you win, remember? I will never forget that,' she said, and we kissed.

I felt like a condemned man. Not only was I going to lose Laura and Wendy, but the only noble way to do it was to get beaten up in the process. Everything, suddenly, felt flat. We decided to leave shortly after lunch. You can push a good thing too far, and neither of us wanted the memory of an unforgettable weekend to be tarnished just because the transience of all things was starting to become all too apparent to me.

As we joined the M4, Wendy, trying to lift my mood, suggested,

'Why don't we stop off at your place on the way back? I feel like I know you a lot better now and I'm curious to see where you live, just to see if your house in real life looks like it does in my imagination.'

I lived roughly halfway between where we were and Wendy's house, so a stop-off wouldn't involve too significant a detour and it would mean I got to keep Wendy a little while longer. I explained, though, that Rachel might be there doing some work and it would raise some awkward questions if we trooped in together. Wendy went quiet and I could sense the gears turning in her head.

'What if...,' she had a twinkle in her eye. 'What if, if Rachel is there, we have a little wrestling match? I'm not going to catfight her, but I think we'd all be interested to see who would come out on top in a wrestling match, and I would like to give you some solid evidence about my fighting abilities just so I can back up my performance in the fantasies you're going to be having about me. We could tell her that I e-mailed you a secret challenge and that we planned it as a surprise for her because she was so impressive the other day. I'll even fight her in my lingerie if you like.'

The thought of Wendy fighting Rachel in the garter belt which she had used to seal my infidelity earlier that weekend was irresistible.

'And what if she's not there?'

'Then I'll wear it again anyway. We can at least say goodbye to each other properly, in your own bed. I'd like that.'

Wendy was very persuasive.

As I opened my front door, with Wendy close behind, I didn't know whether to wish that Rachel was there or not. It was a win/win situation really. We crept up the stairs together with the intention of surprising her if we found her working in the spare room where I had my desk and computer. Rounding the stairs at the top, I caught sight of Rachel in my bedroom. She was on the bed on all fours, naked, her eyes closed and her mouth open, pushing herself slowly and tantalisingly back on to the cock of a man whose face I could not see.

'Oh, my fucking God...Yes... Yes... Yes! Own me! Oh God, fuck me, I'm yours!' she cried as she hit the peak of an orgasm that had clearly been building for some time, and he grunted his load into her.

I moved into view.

'Oh, my God.' said Kev, noticing our arrival just after he came.

I left Kev and Wendy and Rachel there without uttering a word. My house of cards had come tumbling down. I had lost the three women I loved in the space of three hours. I walked for miles. Maybe it was two hours, maybe it was three hours, maybe four; my thoughts flitted back and forth between the heaven that had been Saturday and the horror show that was now. I was angry and numb at the same time. As I reapproached my house in the dark, I knew that I just wanted them to be gone.

There was no sign of Kev or Wendy, but Rachel was still there in the kitchen. She had waited for me and she had been crying. We just looked at each other.

'It was one time only,' she pleaded after about a minute's silence. 'It was just revenge. I know everything. About you, and Wendy, and Laura. And the pregnancy.'

Barely taking in what she had said, I ordered her upstairs. We reached the bedroom, and I slammed the door shut. When I slammed her against the door - with as much force as she had once slung Mel into a plasterboard wall - and kissed her on the lips, she responded voraciously. We ripped each other's clothes off, and I took her hard. If there was anything of Kev still inside of her, I was going to eradicate every trace. I grabbed her hair from behind as I had once done to Laura, only this time it was rougher, much rougher. It was hate-sex, pure and simple.

'You fucking slut,' I kept repeating as I thrust into her. 'You fucking slut.'

We both came for the second time that day, and then I told her to leave.

CHAPTER 7 LIVES IN THE BALANCE

I don't recall the precise mechanics of how Rachel had uncovered not only my infidelity, but also the existence of an embryo I knew nothing about. Maybe I never found out. As I think back to it, I realise that I do not know whether my downfall was the outcome of chance; or whether it was the deliberate outcome of a ploy initiated by Mel, Kev, Laura or, God forbid, even Wendy. Whatever the mechanism, my comeuppance could not have been any more brutal and complete - and I hadn't even met my prospective fight opponent yet.

My first instinct was to talk to Laura, but I didn't feel like talking to anyone that night. Instead, I sent her an e-mail.

Dear Laura,

Wendy must have told you everything. We need to talk. Soon?

T.

... and stared at my Inbox in vain hope of reply until the early hours. I didn't even know what I was going to say to her if she agreed.

Laura deigned to reply just after 11am the next morning.

Hey you, mr sexmachine

2pm next Thursday, here. Wendy and Mel will make them-selves scarce. Both probably too mortified to see you, anyway.

I've got a proposition for you. Don't phone, just come.

L.

P.S. It goes without saying: Leave that bitch at home if she hasn't already left you.

Wendy's prediction looked like it might be being fulfilled faster than either of us could have imagined.

Rachel and I were over. It may have felt like love at the time, but if it truly had been, I wouldn't have done what I had, and she would not have taken such a revenge. There was no escaping that. My mood settled and I accustomed myself to the idea that things would, and could, never be the same.

The letter I wrote to Rachel was conciliatory. There was no chance of a reunion, but I wanted her to know that she would always have a place in my heart. You can't have a relationship with someone for almost a year without it leaving some kind of permanent mark, especially given the intensity of the experiences we had been through to-gether. I accepted responsibility for my actions and made it clear I did not expect, want or deserve any kind of for-giveness. I also told her that she was one of the most im-pressive women I had ever had the privilege of knowing; that the crucible of catfighting had only made me admire her more; and that the previous six months had been a wild ride I would never forget or regret.

I expected no reply; nor did I receive one.

Wendy sent me a message to say that she was thinking of me, and that she hoped we would see each other again.

I couldn't stay there, in that house on my own, so I travelled back to Bath for the week leading up to my arranged date with destiny. If Laura was going to suggest that I fight for her again, I decided that I would do it. It would be my penance for what I had put Rachel through, and if it helped Laura move on from me, there would at least be some point to my likely defeat. I deserved to be forgotten by her.

Maybe a part of me even wanted to fight on behalf of the embryo inside her. I wasn't completely resigned to its fate and mine. If I was going to be in another fight for Laura, I resolved to do my best to win it, so I spent the week training relentlessly outside in the muggy August heat: three workouts a day, each consisting of running, push-ups and shadow boxing. If I had to go down, I would do go down fighting with the courage that both Rachel and Mel had displayed during their own beatings.

I didn't know what to expect from Laura when I pulled up outside her house. Would the guy who she might be lining up to fight me be there to? Would she be annoyed that I had spent that cataclysmic weekend in Bath with Wendy? Would she be pleased that Rachel and I had broken up? Would she want to talk about her pregnancy, if indeed it had not already been terminated? In the back of my mind, I even wondered if there was some small chance that she and I might yet have a future together.

'Hey, lover boy,' she said sarcastically on opening the door. She was as attractive as ever, but there was a gravity, even a sadness, about her I had not seen before. I don't remember her clothes, though I am sure her midriff was again on display. Laura turned away and walked back to the kitchen, leaving me to close the front door. I followed her in, and we looked at each other, not knowing what to say. At least my prospective replacement was not here, as far as I could tell.

'Have you broken up with her?' she asked.

Rachel was nameless again. I nodded.

'How will I ever fight her again now?'

She looked frustrated.

'You don't need to,' I said. 'You already proved you were better once. You don't need to do it again.'

'Do you still think about it?'

A glimmer of a smile played on her lips.

'All the time.'

I moved closer, touched her face and we kissed. There was a tenderness about it.

'Why didn't you tell me you were pregnant?' I asked, not able to stop myself.

She stepped back.

'Is it relevant?'

'Is it mine?'

'Yes, of course it's yours. The one and only time I fuck without a condom and would-you-believe-it? I'm never doing that again.'

'Are you still pregnant?'

'For now. Why? Do you want to make an honest woman out of me, or something?'

I went to embrace her, but she took another step back and turned away from me.

'I'm too young for this!' she exclaimed, and suddenly burst into tears.

It was the first time I had ever seen her cry. She let me take her in my arms at the second attempt, and I reminded myself that she was only twenty-one. I felt our age difference, probably for the first time. Suddenly, she seemed girlish. We stood in silent embrace for a couple of minutes.

'It's okay,' I assured her. I told her I would support her in whatever she decided to do.

'What do you want?' she asked.

Not knowing what I wanted had got me into this situation in the first place. Rachel and I were history. Wendy and I were non-starters. All I had left was the hope of a future with Laura. She had given me the most mind-blowing sex I had ever known, but despite that, I did not really know who she was. It had been all about the passion and little else. I omitted to tell her that I wanted her to have the baby and that I would stand by her if she did.

'I want you...,'

I was going to say that I wanted her because I did. Instead, I said,

'I want you to be happy, and if I could make you happy, I would.'

She nodded, separated from me, and walked to the other side of the kitchen.

'I'm not mad about it,' she said, giving away that she

probably was, 'but why did you take Wendy to Bath that weekend?'

I explained that I had felt a bond with Wendy from the first moment that I saw her, and that I wanted to see if there was anything there, even if it meant putting my relationship with Rachel at risk.

'And was there?'

'There was, but more on my side. She made it perfectly clear that it wasn't enough for her.'

Maybe it was the sadness on my own face that caused Laura's to crumple. She burst into tears again.

'I wanted it to be me!'

'Oh fuck, Laura. Why didn't I ask you? I didn't even know you wanted to.'

I took her in my arms again, knowing that if she had come with me that weekend instead of Wendy, I would forever have wondered.

'Is it too late?' I asked.

She looked at the floor and thought for a long time. Lives hung in the balance.

'I think we might have missed our moment,' she said, re-composing herself and stepping back.

Then, after another long silence,

'...There's someone else.'

I wasn't going to make her ask. I wanted to make it easy for her.

'Does he realise he's going to have to fight me for you?'

She looked up, and her face didn't know whether to be happy or sad. I wondered if it was from the relief of not having to manipulate me into the fight herself, or because she knew the extent of the impending mismatch.

'If he wins and I end up losing you,' I continued, 'I just want you to know that I would fight for you every single day of the week. I know we don't even know each other all that well - I've seen you, what, six times now? - but you are the sexiest woman I have ever met. You blow the rest of them out of the water.'

I meant it. Wendy may have been the most beautiful woman I had ever seen, but something about Laura made me want to fuck her on sight. She looked at me with desire and intent, and I wondered if it was for the last time.

'How about I call him now, and then maybe we can do it one more time before you go into battle for me?'

I took a deep breath and nodded.

I had brought the trunks in which I had fought Kev, and now I sat in them, at the end of Laura's bed, pulling a black t-shirt over my torso. Laura and I then shifted the desk and chair into Mel's room. She brought back duvets from Mel's room and Wendy's. We spread them over the floor, together with the one from Laura's bed, and laughed when we noticed that the sheet underneath it was still moist from our rapture. We placed a beanbag in two of the corners. It didn't take much to get the room ready.

He was coming at 6pm, half an hour away.

A key in the door was followed by hushed voices as Wendy and Mel returned from wherever they had been. They sensed my presence. Laura went down to tell them what was happening, and I prepared to meet my fate.

Weak from my exertions with Laura, I felt like a condemned man in a cell the night before he climbs the gallows.

My first visitor was Mel. When she came in, I stood. Dressed in more understated attire since the last time I had seen her, she reminded me more of the person I first met on that February night than the Barbie doll who had riled, and then been ravaged by, Rachel. She was still sexy, but I remembered her destruction and that dropped her to the bottom of the pecking order.

'Hey,' she said, embarrassed.

'Hey,' I said back.

We didn't know what else to say. This was the first time we had spoken since she had been beaten up – there is no other way to express it – by Rachel. It was the first time we had been alone together in a room since that night downstairs when we had very nearly given in to temptation.

'How are you, Mel?'

Nearly a month had gone by since she had met her match in this room. If that fight had had a different outcome, we would have become lovers in the room adjoining this one. I was sure of that now.

'I'm cool. Sorry I couldn't say anything to you after last time.'

I told her it was okay and said that I was pleased to see her in full health. Then I asked her if she was going to be watching later.

'I would like to if you're okay with it.'

'Have you met him before?'

She blushed and nodded.

'So, who will you be supporting?'

'I want you both to win, really. I'll be happy for whoever wins and sad for whoever loses.'

I didn't want her pity.

'Mel, if I lose, this will probably be the last time we see each other,' I said.

I walked across and hugged her, and told her that, despite her loss to Rachel, I still thought she was one of the coolest people I had ever met; and that I admired her for how she handled herself before, during and after her fight.

'Great fights take two people, and you made it as much as Rachel did. Even if you didn't win, I still think you're completely amazing.'

That much was true. Though she was not in the same league as the women who had proved themselves to be superior catfighters, as far as I was concerned Mel was still a league above most of those who would never dare to put it on the line like she had. She had lost but she had done it with conviction and attitude, and that made her special to me.

She tried to suppress a smile and looked away, and I felt good that what I said had mattered to her.

'I'm sorry about what she did to you with Kev,' she said, slightly embarrassed.

There were no secrets.

'Take care,' I said as she turned to leave.

'You too.'

She looked at me as though she were saying goodbye to a dying man, and was gone.

Laura was next. We sat on the bed where we had made love just an hour or so earlier.

'I think he's going to be here in about ten minutes, so I just wanted to come and…'

She didn't finish her sentence, but in my head, I said it for her,

' … say goodbye.'

Her face was red with excitement and I thought I saw her hands shaking.

'Laura, I'm going to fight for you with every breath in my body, but I know it's going to be a tall order. If I win, I want you to have the baby and I want to marry you. If he beats me, then he will deserve you and I accept that I'll just have to walk away if that's what you really want. You deserve the best. You once told me that you and I were born to fuck each other senseless, and we did that. I wish I had taken you to Bath with me, but we went places that I didn't even know existed and that I doubt I will ever go to with anyone else. If I lose, I won't have many regrets about what has happened over the last few months but I will regret one thing, which is that, although I got to know your body, I never discovered who you truly are.'

She didn't say anything. We both stood up, and we embraced tightly, and she cried again on my shoulder. And then she left.

And finally, Wendy. Her first words to me were,

'Are you okay?'

I assured her I was, and we held each other close for a long time. The doorbell rang, and I heard a man's voice downstairs. I breathed in Wendy's perfume. Whereas Mel's had possessed the fragrance of candy floss, Wendy's was floral. I imagined her wearing it throughout the entirety of a life spent with me. She had told me in Bath it was called Grand Amour by Annick Goutal. I own a bottle of it today, my one and only souvenir of her.

'I'm so sorry we didn't get to say goodbye properly after that fabulous weekend,' she said. 'I'm not sure that I have ever enjoyed a weekend as much as that one until we had to come home, and I will treasure it always. I never got to say 'thank you' for it, so thank you. I'm sorry it ended like it did.'

I told her that all good things must come to an end sooner or later, and that grief is just the price we pay for love. I sensed I was only just beginning to pay it.

'Laura is normally in the corner of 'the old boyfriend',' said Wendy, but she's agreed to let me do it this time, but only if you don't have any objections?'

She looked for my reaction.

'I wouldn't want it any other way.'

She held out her hand. I took it, pressed it to my lips and then sat down with her on the bed, still holding it. A few minutes later, we heard footsteps on the stairs.

Mel knocked, slipped through the half-open door, and came to sit on the bed. I rose and went to my corner.

Then Laura.

'I'd like you to meet Rob,' she said before he had even come in.

She was nervous, like a daughter introducing a prospective boyfriend to her father. He walked in, surveyed the room and looked over to me. I approached and shook his hand, looking him directly in the eye. So, this was the guy who Laura had lined up to replace me.

At 6'2" or so, Rob had at least three inches on me. He probably outweighed me by 20 pounds as well. I guessed he was a similar age to all the others in the room, so eight, maybe even nine years younger than me. He wore a Union Jack t-shirt which moulded itself tightly to the contours of his wide chest, and black speedos which were barely adequate to disguise his obvious excitement for the task at hand. He sniffed and nodded.

'Nice to meet you mate. She tells me you've done this before.'

I nodded back. He looked as strong as a powerlifter and his square jaw gave him an air of self-confidence as well as intimidation. The short spiky hair must have been dyed blonde given the darkness at its roots. He looked down at Laura, who gazed up at him in admiration.

'Let's get to it, shall we?' he said, moving instinctively to his own corner, removing his shirt and doing squat repetitions as he faced me.

He had a deep tan and the rippling muscles on his chest and abdomen had already captivated the attention of Mel and Wendy.

'Come to the centre, guys,' invited Laura, her voice quavering with nerves.

I removed my shirt and went to face him. He towered over me and smirked as he looked down. My body compared badly. Though I lifted, I was not as chiselled. Though I was not exactly pale, his tan put mine in the shade.

Laura held in her hand the same piece of paper that contained the rules from my bout with Kevin. It shook as she read from it.

'Guys, this is a best-of-five submission wrestling contest, with a two-sub margin needed for victory. Rounds will last three minutes with breaks of five minutes. You may use wrestling holds; you may body-punch or slap; you may kick; knee-strikes are also allowed. You may pull hair. BUT: No strikes to the face; no joint locks; no biting or gouging; no choking; no attacks to the balls. After a submission, you have ten seconds to be ready to resume the match or you will be counted out. I am the referee, and the prize. The winner of this fight wins me, and I won't be letting them go anywhere until they have fucked me senseless at least once tonight. One of you is going to be a very lucky guy.'

His eyes widened and he licked his lips lasciviously. Laura giggled. The hell was I going to let him have her that easily.

'Do you have anything to say to Rob?' Laura asked me.

'May the best man win her.'

'Rob?' she asked.

'You're too old for her anyway, mate.'

He grabbed his erect crotch through the fabric of his Speedos and shook it briefly in his hand. Laura giggled again. I turned and went back to my corner. I so badly wanted to flatten this motherfucker.

'Guys! I want the winner! Fight for me!' yelled Laura.

I felt his strength from the very first contact. He threw me, judoka-like, and I landed heavily on my back in the middle of the room. He took his time. Dazed, I got to my hands and knees as he paraded around the room, milking their attention. I was pulled up in a headlock, lifted off the floor, rolled backwards and sent crashing across the floor. I landed with my legs halfway up the wall. I was on autopilot. I heard the shouts around me from all three girls, but I didn't know what they were saying. The only one that I could make out as I was picked up and tossed down repeatedly onto the floor was Laura's.

'Oh God! Oh God!'

She thought he was killing me. So did I. I don't know how many times I was picked up, thrown, landed on. I don't know how many times my arms and thighs were stamped on, but it seemed never-ending. I don't know how many punches I took. They told me afterwards that it wasn't totally one-sided, but I have no recollection of putting up any resistance.

My next memory is of opening my eyes to see Wendy bending over me, stroking my forehead. They didn't tell me how it had happened, but I must have been counted out. I was lying in the neutral corner, not having survived even a single round. Mel would have known the ignominy. My entire body felt broken and I wondered how I was ever going to get back into my car and drive home.

'What happened?'

'Let's just say you didn't win,' said Wendy sympathetically, but she struggled to look me in the eyes.

She helped me sit up and offered me water. There was no sign of Mel but the bedroom door was open. Across the room, those two were on the bed, oblivious to us. Wendy shook her head with irritation. As she helped me to my feet and from the room, I looked back. They glanced momentarily across as I stood at the door with her, and then lost themselves in each other again.

◆ ◆ ◆

I woke up in a strange bed, on my own, still wearing my t-shirt and trunks from the fight. Fumbling in the darkness, I eventually managed to locate a light switch. It was the first and only time I ever saw her room, but Wendy's touch was obvious. Her soul infused the posters, the books and the music CDs. Her unmistakeable scent hung in the air too. According to my watch, which I found on a pile of my clothes on the floor, it was just before midnight. There were voices overhead. I got dressed through the pain, collected my things together and hobbled out of that house, stumbling through the downstairs darkness without seeing anyone. My body was sore, my neck and shoulders ached, and my head was thumping but I had to leave. I squeezed myself into the car, flinching from my injuries and remembered how Rachel had left the house in similar shame half a year previously. I took one final look back to the upstairs window and saw the curtains twitch.

It was just about possible to operate the controls without the pain becoming excessive, but I drove slowly, thanking God that there was so little traffic. It was still dark when I reached home. I climbed the stairs, and collapsed into my own bed, numb.

CHAPTER 8:
THE VISIT

Summer was taking its leave. It was the first day of the Late Summer Bank Holiday weekend, and I was on my own. School was to resume in three days' time and I spent the day preparing. It had been over a week since I had lost everything, and my body, covered in yellowed bruises, was still sore to the touch. I suppose it was miraculous that I had emerged from that battle without any fractures or other serious damage, so I was grateful for that, at least.

In the late afternoon, I made myself a coffee and took it to the patio table outside. It brought back memories of when I and Rachel had sat there on a warm springtime day in late March and she had noticed other bruises. I taught at the same school as Rachel, and I felt apprehensive about how we would cope when we inevitably saw each other again. I wondered if she would somehow have learned about my annihilation at the hands and feet of Rob.

I reflected over the previous six months. I had won everything; I had lost everything; I had tasted victory and devastation; passion and humiliation. And I had shared it with four remarkable young women who had now fallen out of my life. All that remained were memories, but my God, they were memories to last a lifetime. With hindsight, would I have done it all again, considering the emptiness which now faced me? Without a shadow of a doubt. In my letter to Rachel, I had described cat-fighting as a crucible, and it was definitely that. We had discovered things about ourselves and each other which most people never dare to confront. We had uncovered our Shadows; we had opened ourselves to risk and pain; some of us had experienced the sadistic pleasure of humbling a rival; and some of us had tasted the humiliation of defeat, in love or war or both.

There could be no happy ending. Catfighting thrills you and it kills you, whether you are a participant or an observer. I fantasised about Hollywood endings. Maybe Laura and Rachel would somehow engineer a rematch between themselves and invite me to watch as a truly impartial observer, and Rachel would exact her revenge. But as I imagined it, I realised I wouldn't have been impartial. I would have wanted Laura to prevail again in the same brutal manner as before. I bore no malice towards Rachel. It was my fault that we had broken up. But I was still, and would always be, under Laura's spell because of that February night. She may have dispensed with me for good, but I didn't want that spell ever to be broken.

I fantasised about the embryo inside Laura growing up to do battle with an imaginary child I had created with Rachel during our episode of hate-sex. Half-sisters, the daughter of Laura versus the daughter of Rachel, fighting one another in an echo of history. Hollywood.

I still occasionally wonder about it today. They would both be about twenty-three years old now, in their cat-fighting prime.

My tapes from Crystal and DWW, once viewed almost daily, had lain untouched for the last six months. They paled into insignificance compared with the scenes I had tasted in real life, re-lived in memory and now imagined in fantasy.

And what about Wendy versus Mel? What a battle that would be, but every time I played it over in my mind, Wendy came out on top, beating her as convincingly as Rachel had.

Wendy versus Rachel? Those fantasies came out fifty-fifty. The one battle that was always too painful and difficult for me to contemplate was Laura versus Wendy. Even now, I can't do it. These thoughts triggered a memory of a dream I had had from the previous night, where Wendy had fought a faceless foe, although she was no longer called Wendy. Instead, she fought under the name of Vertu. The fight had been forgotten as dreams usually are, but her name had stayed with me.

The doorbell roused me from my reverie. Two figures lurked behind the frosted glass window of the front door, and I opened it, ready to give Jehovah's witnesses a piece of my mind.

'You didn't even say goodbye.'

Wendy pouted at me. Rachel was standing behind her, sheepishly. I no longer knew where the line between real life and fantasy began and ended.

I stared at them both on my doorstep, uncomprehending.

'Are you going to invite us in?' suggested Wendy.

I nodded, dumbfounded, and led them through to my

small living room.

'What are you doing here?' I asked, still in shock, before they had even sat down.

Wendy put her arms around me in the way a mother might hug a child who had grazed his knee.

'We just wanted to know you're okay.'

I closed my eyes. It felt good to be in her arms again, so totally unexpectedly, and to lose myself for a few seconds in her distinctive scent. She stepped back and Rachel stepped forward. We hadn't spoken since that fateful Sunday. She looked directly into eyes which were already watery, and a silent tear rolled down both of our cheeks as we embraced each other. There was an unspoken understanding that, if we would never be lovers again, we could at least be friends.

'I heard about it,' she whispered.

They were the first words I had heard her speak in nearly three weeks.

'You didn't need to do that.'

She wouldn't have understood if I told her that I did. She kissed me on the cheek.

'Do you think we could have a cup of tea?' said Wendy, looking around the room, perhaps to see how well it conformed to her expectations.

'It's okay, I'll get it. I know where everything is,' said Rachel, a touch sadly.

I sat down on the sofa with Wendy.

'I was worried about you,' she said. 'Are you really, okay? When I got back you were gone, and I hated not being able to say goodbye to you.'

I was careful not to ask where she had gone just in case the answer killed me.

'I feel better when you're around,' I replied, and she smiled. 'How's Laura?'

She took hold of my hand and her energy flowed into me again.

'She's not pregnant anymore,' she said, 'I'm sorry,' breaking the news as gently as the most well-trained doctor.

I shrugged. What else could I have expected? Nevertheless, a wave of ineffable sadness engulfed me, and I had to close my eyes for a few moments to collect my thoughts. She kept her hand on mine until I could open them again.

'I don't understand what you're doing here with Rachel, though.'

The incongruity of seeing them together had just dawned on me. They had only met each other once before, and even then, only exchanged a few words. Wendy cottoned on.

'Ah. You know me, don't you?'

She waited as the penny dropped.

I did know Wendy. I knew her well enough to know that she was as interested in women as she was in men. I knew her well enough to understand that she and Rachel had probably spent yesterday and today exploring each other in the same way that Wendy and I had explored each other during that weekend in Bath.

'Oh, I see. I get it.'

Wendy grinned.

Rachel came in and it was clear to her what we were discussing. As far as I knew, Rachel had never considered herself to be anything other than heterosexual, but I didn't blame her for falling for Wendy's seductive, bohemian charms. Rachel blushed, and Wendy and I both smiled across at her as she wriggled on her chair in discomfort.

'Wow. We've all fucked each other, haven't we?' I said, and we all burst out laughing.

'It's actually a little bit more complicated than that,' said Rachel when the laughter had subsided. 'We almost made love earlier today but then we realised that first of all, we have to make war.'

It was a strange drug.

I looked across at Wendy, confused, to see if she understood and agreed with what was being said. She shrugged her shoulders, smiled and nodded.

'What are you saying?' I asked incredulously.

'We like each other, but we need to fight each other first, and we want you to watch it and intervene if necessary,' Wendy confirmed.

My head was spinning.

'What? Why?'

'Why do guys always have to be asking why?' said Wendy, apparently exasperated with me. 'I don't know. She doesn't know. We can't explain it.'

Rachel nodded in agreement.

'So, you want to have the wrestling match we were talking about that day we came back?'

'No. We want a catfight. I know I said I would never do it, but I must. I need to fight her. She needs to fight me. We're still harbouring some resentment towards each other and, to be frank, we need to find out who's best when it really comes down to it. Maybe it will turn into a wrestling match but right now I want to catfight Rachel, and she definitely wants to catfight me. We have to hurt each other a little bit more before we can love each other, I think. Sorry, it sounds stupid. I can't explain it. It's just one of those things. No matter how much I like Rachel, I still want to come out on top in my fantasies and yours, and in real life too, and I think she feels the same way.'

Rachel gazed at Wendy and nodded in agreement with everything she said.

'Maybe I'm also still mad at her for what she did to you,' Wendy continued. 'It's none of my business, I know, but that rankled with me, even though I was probably the cause of it. The look on your face when you saw...'

Wendy stopped mid-sentence. She looked across to the window, at a loss for words. Rachel also looked out of the window and choked back her own tears.

'It's not like there isn't something I'm finding it hard to forgive you for either,' she said to Wendy after she had collected herself, 'You changed my life when you two spent that weekend together.'

Wendy nodded unapologetically.

'I'm not proud that I hurt you but I would do it again to-morrow,' she said.

I loved Wendy for her honesty, no matter how stone-cold hurtful it could be.

'If I hadn't seduced your boyfriend, I wouldn't have se-duced you either, and we wouldn't be sitting here now. Both of you have brought a lot of joy to my life and I know it has been at the expense of causing you a lot of pain. But perhaps I saved you from hurting each other even more in the future.'

Rachel looked back at me, and we wondered.

'Wendy and I need to properly have this out,' Rachel said after a few moments. 'Then the way would be clear for us to be proper friends. Right now, the past is stopping us. This isn't a Laura situation at all,' Rachel continued. 'We genuinely like each other but I still bitterly resent what she did. We can, and I hope will, be friends, but this has just got to happen first. She put me in my place when she went off with you and now I want to do the same to her. We have all learned enough about catfighting by now to know that it could get out of hand if our emotions get the better of us, and they probably will, but Wendy and I trust you more than anyone to stop it before it goes too far. What do you think?'

They both looked at me, imploring me to be the man in the middle. I had never seen Wendy fight. I was dying to see her fight, but I was satisfied with the fifty-fifties that played out in my imagination. I wasn't sure I could take the sight of them catfighting each other in real life, especially if it was going to be anything like the violence I had witnessed in Rachel's previous two contests. I didn't say anything.

'We will only ever do this once, and if you weren't around, we wouldn't even consider it at all,' said Wendy. 'Please?'

And that is how I came to referee the catfight to end all catfights.

When they had talked about it before visiting me, Rachel

had suggested that my bedroom would just about suffice for their intended bout. It was nowhere near as suitable as Laura's room, but it would do. My double-bed stood in the middle of the room, its headboard against a wall, and there were less than a couple of metres clearance in each direction outwards from it, but the room's fitted wardrobes meant that it was safe from protruding furniture. I could move my nightstand into the other room. Most of the action would take place on the bed, I surmised, but as these two beautiful women were now prospective lovers in addition to being rivals with a grudge to settle, it somehow seemed appropriate. It was easy enough to cover the small amount of floor space with the duvet from my bed and some spare sheets.

I wanted to know what rules they had planned.

'Standard catfight rules,' said Rachel, 'just like we had against Mel and Laura, but let's not do timed rounds. We go at it until someone submits and then we'll rest until we're ready to restart.'

'I don't want you body-punching or even face-slapping,' I said firmly.

They nodded in agreement, although I sensed Rachel's reluctance.

'We don't have a fixed number of submissions in mind, either' added Wendy. 'We'll fight for submissions, but let's not say how many. If this goes the way we want it to go, we will both know when it's over.'

They both looked deadly serious. I couldn't help wondering whether they were setting up a 'work' as a consolation prize for me, the man who had lost everything. They would soon dispel my doubts.

'We want the build-up and everything,' said Rachel. 'Let's get some tension going so that we can really fight it out of our systems.'

Wendy nodded and laughed.

'You'll probably want to have a conversation with her before we start,' said Wendy. 'Come and see me afterwards, when she's ready, because I'd like to talk to you too.'

Anticipating my agreement, they had already brought costumes ready to change into. Rachel prepared herself in the bathroom, and Wendy used the spare room that I used for my schoolwork. I waited in the bedroom, trying to work out what was going on and why they were doing it. It was pointless and unexplainable, but I resolved not to stand in the way.

Rachel knocked on the door of the bedroom in which we had once been lovers and I invited her in. She looked sheepish to be back in the familiarity of this room under such different circumstances. She was wearing a red bikini which I didn't recall having seen before and looked radiant. For a moment I regretted everything. We were suited in so many ways and I was so impressed by who she had become. But though she still turned me on, I could no longer see a future for us. I was haunted by that image of her on this bed with Kev and I knew it would never leave me. Furthermore, I knew that even at our sexual peak, I had not quite reached the indescribable heights that I had with Laura, nor had I ever been as infatuated with her as I was with Wendy. We had become ex-lovers who still liked each other. I still loved her, even, but not enough, and it was right to let her go.

'Hey. You look amazing.'

'Thanks. Are we doing the right thing, do you think?'

'Does it feel right?'

'Yes.'

'Then trust it. Sometimes you just have to go with your heart.' There was a silence. 'Did you get the letter I sent you? I meant every word.'

She nodded.

'It was lovely.' She paused. 'We ruined it all, though, didn't we?'

'Rach, we can't think like that. I'm grateful for every day that I had with you. We have to move on, but we'll always be friends.'

There was another silence, but it was a comfortable one.

'It's weird that we both want to fuck Wendy, isn't it?' she said.

We both laughed.

'And now she and I are going to fight. I suppose I'll never get that rematch with Laura now, so she'll have to do instead. I need to fight her before I can love her, and I know she feels the same way about me. Don't let us hurt each other too much, though, will you?'

'I promise. You're both too special to me. But you know what Wendy's like, don't you? Don't go falling in love with her if you can help it. If she doesn't hurt you in the catfight, she'll hurt you afterwards.'

'I know. If I can love you without being in love with you anymore, I can do the same with her.'

I walked over and embraced her, but kissing was no longer a part of our shared vocabulary. As we let go, she stepped back and looked me squarely in the eye.

'You'd better believe I'm going to win this. I like her, but something inside me really wants to smash her up!'

We both laughed. She combined the animal and the spiritual as well as anyone I ever met. In fact, her only competition in that regard was Wendy.

I went into the spare room to see her opponent. Wendy was perusing my CD shelves in a leopard-skin patterned two-piece bikini. My God, how was I ever going to get her out of my system?

'I like you even more now,' she said, holding up Dylan's 'Blonde on Blonde'.

'No pillbox hat then?' I joked. I will never know if she got the reference. 'You look incredible.'

'Thank you,' she smiled, 'I've done some crazy things, but this just about tops them all. I am so excited. In fact, I'm so nervous I can barely stand up.'

Another wave of sadness swept over me. Somehow, I knew that this was the last conversation that she and I would ever have alone together. I told her so. She looked at me with sad eyes. I knew her attraction towards me had faded since my humiliation in the fight with Rob.

'I love both of you. I know that I helped to fuck up your relationship with Rachel, but I was helpless to resist either of you. My infatuations don't last, though, they never do. I'm still a little bit in love with you, but it's like the song, isn't it?'

She came over to me, draped her arms around my neck and half whispered, half-sung into my ear the first verse from the country classic, *'I'd Rather Leave While I'm in Love.'*

And then she hung on to me tightly. I felt her breasts against my chest and the smoothness of the skin on her lower back, and I was too sad to say anything. She stepped back and took my hand.

'I will never forget you. Until we get this over with, she's a bitch as far as I'm concerned and I really want to impress you. I know she thinks she's going to beat me up, but if I win this catfight, and believe me I will, I'm not leaving without us making love one last time.'

There must have been a moment, at some point in our relationship, when Wendy uttered a sentence that didn't turn me on, but I can't think of one.

CHAPTER 9: FIGHT TO THE FINISH

I led Wendy into the bedroom. They hadn't seen each other in their outfits before and I could sense their mutual attraction. Their determination to demonstrate their superiority over the other was also obvious. They smiled at one another and bit their lips but didn't say anything. I invited them to meet at the foot of the bed. Rachel walked around from the far side. They embraced and stepped back. Wendy took a deep breath and exhaled. She was the more nervous of the two. Rachel looked steadily into her eyes, smiling and moving her neck gracefully from side to side, trying to intimidate. She looked as confident as I had ever seen her. Wendy took another deep breath.

'Girls, you wanted to catfight each other and now it's going to happen. Keep in mind that you are fighting from love, not hate.'

To my relief, they both nodded and smiled at each other.

'This is an unlimited submissions catfight. Each round will end with a submission and then you can both rest until you are ready to go again. If I see either of you taking too much punishment, I will step in and award a submission before either of you gets seriously hurt. You will decide between you when the fight is over. You may use wrestling holds; you may direct slaps only to the body; you may kick; you may pull hair; you may trash-talk. BUT: No punches; no slaps to the face; no joint locks; no biting or gouging; no choking; no attacks to genital regions. Are you ready to do this?'

Their eyes were fixed on each other. They nodded, itching to get their hands on one another.

'I have one more instruction. I want you to begin every round with a kiss and follow every submission with another one.'

'You perv,' said Rachel, grinning at Wendy although the comment was addressed to me.

'I think it's cool,' said Wendy, 'Let's do it.'

'Rach, do you have anything you want to say to Wendy before we start?'

She thought about it.

'Yeah. Wendy, I think you're amazing, and I like you a great deal, but it might not feel like it for however long this fight lasts. We'll be friends afterwards, though, I promise.'

Wendy looked emotional. She bit her lip, and I thought I saw a tear in her eye.

'Is there anything you want to say, Wendy?'

She closed her eyes for a few seconds and nodded before she spoke.

'I'm ready to fight you, bitch. Let's do it.'

'Girls, kiss each other and begin.' They giggled.

Wendy held out her arms and Rachel moved to embrace her. They pecked each other on the lips at first, and then as their passion enveloped them, their lips interlocked. As they did so, their bodies brought force to bear on each other and it was clear that each was struggling to dominate the other as their bodies tipped sideways onto the bed. As a spectator, it was not clear whether they were wrestling or making love. Only their soft moans testified to the immense effort they were exerting upon each other, but as their mouths and bodies connected, their strength evened itself into deadlock. I surveyed the scene from the floor and knew that I was going to have to be alert and agile if I was to avoid them careering into me if the fight ever got off the bed.

I was too absorbed with watching the interplay of their bodies to be able to remember a detailed play-by-play of the whole contest, so will content myself with the action highlights that I can remember from nearly a quarter of a century later. As with the other fights described here, the assembled chronology is often the result of piecing together freeze-frame shards of memory.

Slowly, Wendy manoeuvred herself into initial ascendancy in the contest and worked her way up Rachel's body to eventually smother Rachel's face with her leopard-skin-clad breasts. Rachel's back was pinned to the bed, and Wendy's legs and haunches looked powerful from where I stood. Wendy moved with her characteristic languor and grace, but her movement was backed up by power and determination. Fighting from a defensive position on a bed is much harder than from the floor because there is no firm base to launch from. Rachel's legs dangled over the edge of the bed as Wendy brought her full weight to bear on her torso. Instead of attempting to throw Wendy off, Rachel's best hope was to slither out from beneath her, but Wendy wasn't about to let her escape that easily.

Sensing her superiority in strength, Wendy relaxed into the fight. The leopard lay on top of its red-tinged prey, basking in her dominance. I hadn't expected Wendy's wrestling skills to be as good as they were because although I knew she had practiced with Laura, I hadn't been particularly impressed with Laura's technical ability during her fight with Rachel. Wendy's skills were still rudimentary, but she knew how to stifle her opponent. In the sultry English August evening, it didn't take long for both of their bodies to glisten in a sheen of perspiration, adding to the eroticism of the whole piece. Unable to move from the pin, Rachel struggled for air under Wendy's breasts and after maybe ten minutes of efforts to extricate herself, she eventually gave. It wasn't a spectacular submission from Wendy, but it was hard-earned, and she was delighted with it.

'Submission!' I called, as Rachel tapped.

Instinctively, Wendy kissed Rachel on the lips and they collapsed into each other, laughing. When she looked at me, Wendy tried to suppress a smile of pride. I think she had been slightly afraid coming into the fight, partly because it was her first catfight and partly because of what she had seen Rachel do to Mel. Her relief at having dominated the opening fall was clear.

The second round was not dissimilar. Again, from a kissing start, it was taken straight to the bed; again, Wendy dominated, but this time from behind. She soon had Rachel in a rear body scissors, the crook of her elbow pulling up on Rachel's neck. She was playing with her. Squeeze and let go; squeeze and let go. Rachel didn't have any answers. She was being swamped by Wendy's strength and basic technical holds. Rachel thrashed about on the bed and there were attempts to free herself, but Wendy's wrestling was just too good. I felt that Rachel needed to turn it into a catfight if she was going to have any chance. She must have been thinking the same. Still caught in the rear body scissors, Rachel reached back and planted her hands in Wendy's hair for the first time. The effect was immediate as Wendy screamed out in pain.

'Oww! Fucking let go, bitch,' she swore at Rachel, exerting another squeeze with her legs.

Rachel yanked at the hair again. Another scream from Wendy. It was starting to get real. I hoped my neighbours weren't at home or we would soon be having a visit from the police. Wendy grimaced and applied the scissors for all she was worth, fighting through the pain that Rachel was starting to exert on her head. Then it was Rachel's turn to scream as the pain from the pressure of Wendy's legs around her rib cage suddenly overwhelmed her.

'I submit!' Rachel cried out in agony.

Wendy was two-nil up already. With some concern, she checked that Rachel was okay before getting up and swigging from her water-bottle. A confident Wendy, her body glistening in a leopard-skin bikini, winking at me, is one of the enduring images of my life. On the bed, Rachel may have been smiling but I knew she was annoyed with herself. They rested for ten, maybe fifteen minutes, hardly saying a word, and their diaphragms heaved as they tried to recover their breath.

They had started their fight in the daylight and now it was already pitch dark outside. Rachel needed to alter her tactics if she was to get anything from this match and even avoid complete humiliation, so the way she started the next round came as no surprise to me.

'Kiss, girls,' I commanded, to start the round.

They brushed lips and Wendy went to embrace her but Rachel immediately stunned her by pushing back hard with both hands. Wendy lost her balance, falling backwards against the built-in wardrobe and then down onto the floor, yelping from a mixture of shock and pain from the bump she had just sustained to her head. Rachel was as quick as she had been against Mel to press her advantage in the corner of the room. Straddling Wendy, she resorted to one of her favourite tactics from previous fights. Wendy's head was yanked towards Rachel's crotch and the first body-slaps of the contest found their target. The leopard was under attack.

'Come on bitch. How do you like that? Can you take that? Huh?' Rachel taunted gleefully.

The trash-talk was just that, an addition to the drama but not an indicator of malice. Her palms were finding Wendy's thighs and reddening them, though, just as Laura had done to Rachel in that first catfight. They were hurtful and, for the first time, Wendy tasted Rachel's spite. Wendy's only tactic was to try and hold on to Rachel's arms to reduce their leverage and stop the slaps getting through, but many did, and every time they connected there was the same symphony of sound: a grunt of effort from Rachel, the sound of palm on skin and the ripple of Wendy's yelps. Wendy eventually managed to turn onto her front, but Rachel remained on top and now the slaps made contact with Wendy's back, sides and buttocks. Rachel had dialled up the hurt and was enjoying every second of it. Her victim started to moan, softly at first, but distress slowly crept into Wendy's cries. She was getting hurt and it became difficult to watch.

When Rachel got bored with slapping the body, she yanked up Wendy's head by her hair until Wendy grimaced in pain. The dominant fighter looked over to me to make sure I had a good view of her superiority - and smiled. She didn't need to say it because we both knew what she was thinking. I read her mind.

'You took this bitch away with you for a dirty weekend and look what I'm doing to her now! You chose the wrong woman.'

Wendy may have been in distress, but she was also stubborn, refusing to give as the slaps continued to mark her up. She raised her hands to her face so I couldn't see her crying, but I saw her head as it started to shake uncontrollably. I took a careful look to see if I should call a submission.

'Don't you fucking save her! Do NOT fucking save her!' Rachel yelled, and hit Wendy all the harder.

The slaps to Wendy's legs sounded like firecrackers.

'This is it bitch! Payback time!'

A much harder edge had crept into the insults. Rachel rose to her knees to get better leverage on her slaps and her back was erect and proud. Clenching her teeth, Rachel held nothing back as she focused hurt onto the opponent underneath her.

'I give! I give! I give!' wailed the stunned and frightened Wendy, unable to take any more from the continuous barrage of slaps she had weathered.

Rachel stopped and rolled off, quietly fist-pumping the air without making a big thing of it. She rose to her feet and paced around the room as if she owned it, excited finally to have made her mark on the match, her adrenalin now in full flow. Wendy lay still on the floor for half a minute before hauling herself up in the corner. Tears were running down her face and she was taking deep breaths. Rachel came to wipe them away and embraced her. I thought that might have been the end of the contest, and asked for confirmation from Wendy, but she would not surrender that easily.

'No way! We're only just getting started,' she said.

But it was Rachel who was only just getting started. Wendy, eager to redress the balance, hadn't recovered fully when she agreed to the restart and Rachel took full advantage of her error. As soon as they kissed at the start of the next round, Rachel had her hands in Wendy's hair again and tugged her down with force. Wendy found herself kneeling on the ground with Rachel towering over her, holding her down by her own tangled hair. The momentum of the contest had completely switched, and Rachel was now truly in the ascendent. For the first time, it looked like a contest between a woman against a girl. Every time Wendy tried to get up, Rachel used both hands to yank her back down with a nod of satisfaction and, smiling, she punished her with a vicious kick to her left side. Wendy, on all fours, yelped repeatedly in further torment.

The cycle of punishment was repeated for several slow, bitterly hurtful minutes. Rachel was breaking Wendy physically and mentally, and having been on the receiving end against Laura, she knew the effect she was having. She rubbed it in with her trash-talk.

'Fuck, that hurt you, didn't it? You want some more?

Well, you're getting it, bitch.'

Now there was real venom in her voice. The determined, cruel and retributive grimace on Rachel's face, together with the increasing dejection in Wendy's, suggested that Rachel was exorcising all the demons from her loss to Laura, and then some. She had victory clearly in her sights. Beating up Mel had given her a taste for hurting, and now she was smashing up Wendy, just as she had wished. Rachel was out to humble her, and our weekend in Bath must have fuelled the spiteful shots that she piled up on the increasingly distressed wreckage of her victim's body.

I hated what I was seeing. Wendy was succumbing, and the marks from her punishment had turned the smooth tanned skin of her side red raw.

From her position of dominance, and just by holding Wendy down by her hair, Rachel poured on the pressure and Wendy was tiring badly. Her jaw hung open, her eyes closed and she struggled for breath. The noises emanating from both testified to their effort and pain as one dominated the other. Rachel exhaled with sadistic satisfaction as she pulled down; Wendy yelped as she felt the hair being torn from her scalp; Rachel grunted as she delivered yet another brutal kick to her side; Wendy cried out as it hit home. No longer a fight, it had become an ordeal, a punishment-beating. It was brutal to watch, but Wendy was too proud to give.

'This is more like it! Oh fuck yes, now the boot's on the other foot, eh? This is more like it!' shouted Rachel vindictively.

She was becoming ever more excited by the prospect of an injurious and decisive victory.

'I don't think you can take much more of this can you, bitch?'

With every sickening blow, the mortal Rachel was becoming a goddess, and the goddess Wendy was turning into a humbled, increasing dishevelled mortal. Was this why Rachel had wanted the fight? Had she tricked Aphrodite into having her immortality stolen? Wendy wiped away more tears as she was forced by Rachel to look at the ground from her hands and knees. I thought about stopping it and moved in.

'Don't you fucking dare! Don't you fucking dare! She hasn't submitted yet and that means I can keep going,' Rachel warned me off angrily.

Sadistically, she drove another devastating kick into Wendy's ribcage and Wendy keeled over on her back at the foot of the bed. If Rachel was never going to be able to get her revenge on Laura, she was damn well going to make sure that Wendy would pay the price instead. She had every intention of serving Wendy's head up on a plate for me.

'Ow! Ow! Ow! Ow!' cried Wendy as the pain overwhelmed her.

'Fuck yes!' screamed Rachel.

She was channelling Laura's spirit and didn't even know it.

Then Rachel dragged Wendy up by her hair like a rag doll, just as she had done with Mel, and slung her into the opposite wall. Wendy cried out, slumped to the floor, put her head in her hands and started to sob uncontrollably.

'Come on, bitch!' screamed Rachel, out of her mind.

It was too much. I rushed in and pulled Rachel off her

before she could follow up with what would surely have been the final attack, but not before she had planted another vicious kick into her side which sent Wendy's torso down to the floor.

'Submission!' I called.

Rachel swung away, angry and disgusted at my intervention. She wanted to put it beyond any doubt there and then. I crouched down next to Wendy. I couldn't bear to see her getting hurt. We all knew I had rescued her from certain defeat, or at least delayed it.

'I can't watch any more of this,' I said, stroking her forehead as she had stroked mine nine days earlier.

She put her arms around my neck and cried on my shoulder for a long time.

When I looked up, Rachel was pacing impatiently on her side of the room, in no mood for reconciliation. She wanted to get straight back on Wendy. If this catfight had been taking place under the same rules as the fight against Mel, it would already have been over and I would have declared Rachel the winner by KO. As it was, Rachel was lining up more suffering for the most beautiful girl in the world. Through her tears, Wendy whispered in my ear,

'I can do this. I can still do this.'

I didn't know if she was trying to convince me or herself. I looked behind me to see what the noise was. Rachel had thrown a pillow to the floor and was stamping on it.

'Come on then, you fucking bitch! Get off the fucking floor and let's finish this!' she spat.

An awkward silence descended upon the room.

'I'm fine. I'm not done.'

Wendy wiped her tears away, slowly got to her feet and went to embrace Rachel, who was still enraged.

'Hey, it's me, remember? Damn, you're tough Rachel, but you haven't beaten me yet.'

They kissed, briefly, but it wasn't a kiss between equals. Rachel almost devoured her. They fell on to the bed with Rachel on top, hungry to dominate her, and I wondered if it was going to end here. Wendy was on the verge of total surrender, but Rachel stopped herself and dragged herself away. She wanted a proper victory. She still wanted to hurt Wendy more before she could love her.

They took a long time, maybe half an hour, to recover: Rachel from her exertion and Wendy from her pain. Wendy wanted to embrace her during the rest period but Rachel was having none of it. She was still annoyed with me for having saved Wendy from a certain knockout, but she eventually relaxed, confident of her supremacy and the seemingly inevitable outcome.

Wendy was squarely in her sights, and Rachel's body glowed, looking magnificent against the sheets when she lay on the bed during the interval. I felt my allegiances shift. I wanted to fuck her again. The looks we exchanged revealed a mutual hunger. It was purely animal. For the first time, I feared for Laura's safety if they were ever to meet again, and it excited me. I feared for Wendy too.

Wendy's face was reddened and her hair, which would have been the envy of Helen of Troy at the beginning of the fight, was now an unruly, patchy mess. Her whole body looked like it had been dragged around the walls of Helen's own citadel. A bloody graze on her elbow seeped where she had made impact with the wall, but Wendy waved me away when I offered a Band Aid.

They were barely talking now. Both girls turned in on themselves, lost in private thought. I didn't know Wendy well enough to know what she was thinking, but Rachel was contemplating the finish. After several minutes, she could no longer sit down and paced the room instead, unable to contain her nervous excitement. Wendy watched her from the bed and made her wait.

I told Wendy that if I saw her taking much more punishment in the next round, I would step in again, but sooner than before, and maybe even call the whole thing off. She nodded.

'That won't be necessary,' she said with a quiet yet fiery determination, 'It's two-two. I am still very much in contention and I do not want you getting involved if you can help it. Let's finish this properly. If I lose, I'll go out on my shield, but you haven't seen me get down-and-dirty yet.'

As if to announce her arrival as a fully-fledged catfighter, Wendy removed her bikini top and threw it onto the pillow, revealing erect nipples. Rachel followed suit, her body testifying to her own arousal at the primal electricity that was flowing between them.

Five minutes before we recommenced, the talking stopped completely. Rachel clenched her jaw and I could tell she was visualising bringing the contest to a brutal end. The atmosphere changed as both girls sensed the catfight had reached a critical moment.

'Let's fucking well finish this. Then we can be friends,' said Rachel, standing there by the bed, waiting impatiently.

The look on her face said that she meant business. I

wondered what kind of friendship it could be when one woman has to live with the awareness that the other is her physical superior, having been destroyed by her in combat.

Wendy was going back into the lion's den and I didn't want to see her eaten alive. Rachel was ready for the kill, and Wendy had the look of a half-savaged rabbit. I was prepared to stop the contest within seconds of the restart if I had to.

Round five started as violently as round four had finished. After a brief peck on the lips, Rachel had her hands in Wendy's hair again, but this time Wendy refused to go down. Instead, she used her agility to turn Rachel, and then her brute strength to force her back, slamming her hard against the door. Now Rachel was the one to cry out, loosening her grip on her opponent's hair. Wendy stepped back. Before Rachel could recover, a vicious front kick from Wendy stamped into her stomach, hammering her back into the door, and she sunk to her knees, stunned and hurt. Wendy smiled, then dragged her up by her hair, slammed her back into the door again and planted another kick into exactly the same point of Rachel's mid-section. Rachel slumped a second time and Wendy stepped over, straddled Rachel's neck, grabbed her by the hair and fell gracefully sideways so that her neck was scissored between those powerful thighs.

'You had your chance and you missed it, girl!' she jeered with satisfaction. 'Take a good look at your ex because your world is about to get a lot darker.'

Rachel was looking straight at me and soon her face started to turn grey. Wendy looked at me triumphantly.

I jumped in just before she was gone.

'Let go! Submission!'

I tapped Wendy on her thighs and felt the firmness of her muscles. Wendy grinned back at me. We both knew that she had just graduated from wrestler to catfighter. My allegiance shifted back. Wendy leaned over to console Rachel and kissed her on the lips.

'I didn't mean it,' she said to her apologetically, then turned back to me and grinned again.

For a moment, just one tiny moment, she reminded me of Laura.

On the bed they were friends again, but they were no longer laughing at the pain they were inflicting. Wendy pulled loose strands of beautiful auburn and sun-bleached hair from both of their heads and placed them neatly on the pillow beside me. They rested a long time before the next round, getting their breath back. Both realised it could be decisive. Both were tiring from their efforts and they were both hurting from the damage they had unleashed on each other. It had taken its toll.

'I'll be ready in two minutes,' said Rachel.

She took herself over to a corner of the room and prepared. It was reminiscent of the fight with Mel. She did a shuffle on the spot, stared at the floor and visualised her intent. Meantime, Wendy and I were staring at each other. I wanted her, but she had to win first.

'Am I living up to your expectations?' she asked.

'Surpassing them,' I replied.

She tried and failed to suppress a broad smile.

'I might just finish her this round.'

'Fuck off,' said Rachel, 'I am finishing you.'

They beamed at each other.

They knew the end was in sight. Wendy pulled herself to her feet and mirrored Rachel's pacing on the other side of the bed. It wasn't an attempt to imitate. They were both psyched to finish it and come out on top. It had been nip-and-tuck, and both were contemplating brutalising the other to bring the carnage to a definitive conclusion. Neither was moving with anything like as much energy and freedom as when they had begun the contest.

When I called them forward to start the next round they embraced tightly, breast against breast, as if they both knew the showdown was reaching its climax. They lingered on the kiss, with neither attempting to dominate the beginning of what felt increasingly like the final stanza. Then, as if by mutual agreement, each took a step back. The expressions on their faces changed. Wendy licked her lips. Rachel gritted her teeth. They had both hurt each other and they were hungry to do it again.

'Come on, then!' yelled Rachel and they flew at each other in a flurry of slapping.

It quickly ended up on the bed and their hands found their way back to each other's hair. They grunted and rolled, each trying to exert more pain than they were suffering. Wendy asserted herself as Rachel tired, and she went for Rachel's breasts. In all three of the catfights I had seen, this was the first time I had seen the tactic in use. Rachel shrieked as her left breast was mauled without mercy by the younger, stronger, and now increasingly dominant woman, and Wendy tossed her head back, enjoying Rachel's cries and the power they conferred on her. She had gained her second wind. Rachel was still in the fight, though, and didn't lose her grip of Wendy's hair.

Wendy grimaced. More and more strands of auburn and dark blonde – Rachel's hair had bleached from exposure to summer sunshine – littered the sheet, and both girls grunted as they sought to subdue the other.

Slowly but surely, Wendy turned the screw and started to work Rachel over on the bed, continuing to maul and pinch her body so that she squealed in pain. They rolled off the side nearest the built-in wardrobe, and Wendy landed heavily on top, sweat dripping from her forehead into Rachel's face. Gritting her teeth, and with her forearm now pressed firmly against Rachel's jaw, Wendy pulled Rachel's hair with the other. Their breathing intensified and they grunted and growled at each other like animals from close-quarters. Rachel lay trapped between the bed and the wardrobe and, with less than a metre's clearance, there was no means of escape. A more ruthless fighter might have finished it there, slowly ripping out hair, piece by piece, from Rachel's scalp until there was nothing left. Realising the trouble her opponent was in, a smile spread slowly over Wendy's lips, but she relented.

Instead, she manoeuvred herself so as to straddle Rachel's breasts and then let her hands fly. Now Wendy repaid Rachel for all the shots that she had taken earlier in the contest and savoured the pain she was unleashing. Each slap hit home with malice and Wendy paused between shots to taunt her opponent.

'Huh? You like that, sweetie?! How does that feel, huh?! Not so tough now, are we, eh? Not so fucking tough!'

As her dominance increased, so my sexual attraction raged. The goddess of desire had become the goddess of warfare, and now I wanted to see her punish Rachel. Minutes passed at the side of the bed and the welts on Rachel's body were growing from the violence that Wendy was inflicting at will. Rachel was offering less and less resistance and began to weep softly, yet still would not give. Wendy urged her not to give up, just so that she could prolong the torture.

'Come on, baby. You're not going to submit yet, are you? Don't be such a cry-baby. Don't let him see you like this. Where's your fight gone?' she mocked, between the shots that were now starting to devastate Rachel.

I moved in close, wondering whether to stop it. Rachel's increasingly helpless and fading yelps concerned me and I had a flashback to the way she had given up the ghost against Laura. Alarm bells were ringing in my head when Rachel turned her distressed and tear-stained face to look at me. There was no doubt about the extent of her suffering. Wendy saw me from the corner of her eye. Now she was the one begging me to let it continue.

'Oh, no. Please let's not stop this now. Not yet! I want to finish her properly! Don't let there be any doubt.'

She was in full-on warrior mode. Wendy let go and stood up, hoping it would dissuade me from calling the submission. As she rose to one knee, Rachel's sweat-drenched hair fell over her face and silent tears rolled down both cheeks. Her beauty was being eradicated. Ruthlessly, Wendy moved straight in on her again. Dragging her up and forcing her into the tight corner with her forearm, she exhaled noisily as she drove a knee into the outside of Rachel's left thigh. Rachel cried out loudly and she felt victory ebb away. Realising the damage it had caused, Wendy went for the kill. With a shout, she jackhammered another knee-strike onto the outside of the same thigh and then watched with satisfaction as Rachel howled and collapsed in agony back down to the floor, sobbing loudly. Wendy's callous and triumphant smile left me wondering if she had just delivered two parting gifts from Laura. It must have brought the memories back because Rachel put her hand up to cover her eyes.

Unperturbed, Wendy grabbed and wound Rachel's hair into an untidy makeshift ponytail, wrapping it around her wrist and used it to pull Rachel back up. Now assured of victory, she used it as a lead to drag her, on unsteady hands and knees, from the corner to the duvet at the foot of the bed. From there, she yanked Rachel's head up again like a trophy so that I could clearly see the tears glistening on both cheeks, her face having grown puffy from weeping. Now I could easily imagine Wendy fucking up Laura. The medic had gone missing, and a killer was on the loose.

'Lie down,' Wendy commanded forcefully through gritted teeth, her hand still wrapped around Rachel's hair.

She wasn't playing. It was an ultimatum. Rachel realised it and capitulated immediately, rolling over sadly onto her back like a mistreated dog. Wendy let go. Rachel's resistance was at an end and her body convulsed as sobbing overtook her. The better, stronger woman had established herself. I could have stopped it there, but Wendy wasn't done and I trusted her to finish it with love. She lowered herself onto Rachel. Her taut, powerful thighs straddled the cushions of Rachels breasts, and she slid her buttocks back towards Rachel's chin. Facing her feet, Wendy leaned over, hooked her arms under Rachel's knees and sat back so that her opponent's backside was pulled helplessly into the air.

'Fuck, yes,' said Wendy with satisfaction, echoing Laura.

From her unassailable position, she winked at me.

Her hair was still a mess from the beating she had taken earlier, and her body was still covered with the souvenirs Rachel had left on it, but it gave Wendy a wild look that rendered her even more sensuous.

With Rachel's left leg immobilised and held in place by Wendy's left arm, and her buttocks hanging in the air, Wendy's right hand located the moist airborne crotch of Rachel's bikini bottoms, slid beneath the fabric and stroked. The victress's fingers penetrated her beaten opponent and rubbed gently. Wendy was masterful. In complete thrall to her, Rachel became a willing victim, submitting herself to the superior fighter in orgasmic ecstasy. She sighed, writhed, panted, and wept some more.

'Oh God... Oh God... Oh please, God...Oh, fuck me...,' moaned Rachel as her distress transformed to bliss.

Wendy revelled in it. She was magnificent and incomparable, the ultimate catfight goddess.

After it was clear that Rachel had fully come and had nothing left, Wendy looked over her shoulder and gently asked,

'Is this fight over now?'

Rachel was totally spent.

'Yes, it's over,' she whimpered.

The mortal may have burned the goddess, but the goddess had prevailed.

'Tell me, Rach. Who won? Who fucked who? Who is the catfight queen?'

Wendy even taunted with kindness in her voice.

'You did. Oh Christ, you fucked me. You are the queen!'

Rachel gasped, barely able to get the words out.

Wendy looked at me in triumph, raised her eyebrows and licked her lips. She let go of Rachel's leg and it collapsed to the floor. Then she removed her weight from the belly of her vanquished opponent and leaned over to kiss Rachel on the lips. Rachel, red-faced, lay motionless and overwhelmed, eyes closed, coming to terms with her second taste of destruction. It was over, but this time her conqueress had left her in heaven.

Wendy rose and strode back and forth around the room, still excited, trying to let her adrenalin subside. She shook her head and exhaled long sighs of satisfaction, uttering over and over again, 'Oh, fuck,' before standing victoriously over the still motionless figure of Rachel. She savoured every second.

I took her wrist with my hand and raised it in the air.

'The winner and ultimate catfight queen!' I proclaimed, and then took her in my arms. 'You fucking rock'.

'That was for you,' she whispered, 'I wiped the floor with her, didn't I? I told you I would.'

She said it with pride.

Her body may have borne the scars of war, but when I looked into Wendy's eyes, I saw the epitome of womanhood. She was supreme. She was everything. Aphrodite and Athena, lover and fighter, all rolled into one.

After a few moments, Rachel opened her eyes and Wendy crouched down and, without saying anything, pulled her upright into a sitting position. They sat, their legs across each other's bodies, enveloping one another in a long and genuine embrace.

'Can we be friends now?' Wendy eventually asked, quietly.

'Yes. Always,' said Rachel through her tears.

They sat for several minutes, recomposing themselves, stroking each other tenderly, exchanging care and reassurance. Finally, separating their intertwined legs, Wendy sat Rachel up against the foot of the bed, wiped the hair from her eyes and kissed her tenderly on the lips. Then she glanced over to me.

'You must excuse me,' she said, addressing Rachel, 'but now that I've fucked you, I have a burning need for the referee to fuck me, and I want you to see it.'

Rachel smiled, resigned to the spectacle, and Wendy rose to her feet. I took her hand and led her to the bed. Anchises and proud Aphrodite made love for the last time, and Rachel watched. It was slow, deliberate, gentle and suffused with Love. It couldn't have been any other way given the soreness that raged throughout her triumphant body.

In Paris, a car sped through an underground tunnel.

The three of us lay together, naked and completely exhausted. We had drowned in each other's love and spite, over that summer and over that night. As we gazed up at the ceiling, Wendy, with her ruffled hair spread across the pillow, laughed.

'I can't wait to tell Laura all about this. It will drive her completely crazy.'

Laura's spirit was everywhere. She had merited barely a mention all evening, but she was in all of our minds at different points, consciously or not, and I missed her like hell. I fetched the duvet from the foot of the bed and covered us with it. We slept there, all three of us, to-gether. A contentment settled upon us, but it felt like an end, and someone was missing.

The sound of the front door closing woke me up and I had no idea of the time because my bedside clock, on top of my nightstand, was still in the other room. The pillows next to me were empty; Wendy and Rachel were gone. I won-dered, briefly, if it had all been a dream, but the sheets on the floor and the tufts of auburn and sun-bleached hair which lay upon them were incontrovertible evidence of the previous night's violence. I knew I would see Rachel again when term resumed, but as for Wendy? I tried to recall my final moments with her. She never even said goodbye.

It may have been the year of Cool Britannia but in recent weeks, it had felt more like Cruel Britannia to me most of the time. Now I felt an emptiness that stemmed from an intuitive realisation that the four women who had adorned my life over the previous six months had effect-ively left it, probably forever. My life could never be the same and I missed them already.

I wandered downstairs in the vain hope of finding Wendy and Rachel there but knew I would not. I was not in the habit of watching breakfast TV but I just needed human voices to ease my sense of isolation. Dressed in black, the newsreader was reporting on a car accident overnight in which Diana, Princess of Wales had been killed. It wasn't just me. England woke up as a much sadder place that morning too.

EPILOGUE

Rachel left the school where we worked four months later to go travelling the world again. We hardly conversed during the interim. Although we sometimes saw each other briefly in passing, we were too embarrassed to let our personal and professional lives cross. School broke up on the last day of the Christmas term in December 1997 and as I made my way down the stairs on my walk from classroom to car park, she was waiting at the bottom. I doubt it was a coincidence. We walked into the dark, wet December evening; I wished her luck for the future and reminded her how special she was to me. We embraced for a final time. I couldn't resist asking.

'Are you still in touch with Wendy?'

'We talk now and again,' she said, 'but you were right about her. It was good while it lasted but I'm glad I didn't let myself fall too deeply.'

There was a pause and she looked at me.

'I know what you're thinking,' she said with a glint in her eye.

She knew me too well.

'No. I haven't! Don't you think I would have told you? I think that part of my life might be over. I'm too old for getting knocked around anymore.'

Then Rachel paused, wondering whether she should tell me. She succumbed to the temptation.

'Laura and Wendy had one, though.'

My heart sank yet also beat faster. I didn't want to think of them hurting each other. I couldn't imagine them having a catfight unless they had had some kind of argument beforehand, and even the thought of that left me upset. I cared too much about them now.

'Oh God, really? A catfight? With each other?' I asked, and she nodded. 'Please don't ever tell me what happened or who won,' I pleaded, 'I really don't want to know.'

Rachel laughed and got into her car. I never saw her again.

All of the events described here took place in 1997. The Internet was around but it was still nascent. Social media did not exist and for anyone born post-millennium, it is probably difficult to comprehend how people who spent so much time together - sometimes promising eternal friendship - could just lose contact, but we did. At least, I lost contact with them. I don't know what happened to Rachel, or Mel, or Wendy or Laura. Or the Unfortunate Kev, or the Fuckable Rob, for that matter.

Even in 2021, it would probably be difficult, if not impossible, for me to track them down. Not only did the girls - with one exception - have relatively common surnames, but they would probably have got married and changed them by now. It's even likely they would have done so by the time Facebook went mainstream in 2008, so their original names would have left no social media footprint to facilitate detection.

One of them, however, had a very distinctive surname, and it was impossible for me to resist the temptation to Google her. I tracked down a profile on LinkedIn: the biography and its accompanying picture belonged unmistakeably to Wendy. I don't know if she is married, but she still uses the surname by which I knew her; and she is a partner in a professional practice in Greater London. I'm happy for her. I daresay that, armed with this information, I could find out more if I were sufficiently motivated. Her profile picture shows that she is still beautiful - as much on the inside as on the outside, no doubt - but she is also older. Despite the temptation to contact her, something inside always deters me. She lives on in my memory as a goddess, a catfight queen and the most beautiful twenty-one-year-old ever to walk the planet. May she, and they, stay forever young.

AFTERWORD

I very much hope that you have enjoyed reading this book. My initial reason for writing it was because I found it difficult to identify authentic catfighting novels on Amazon. I am aware that there is a great wealth of free 'catfight fiction' available on the web, especially on forums such as freecatfights.com, but most of them are written in the fantasy genre. There are certainly some very good short stories about authentic apartment-style catfighting available too, but few are as lengthy as the account you have read in these pages.

I would like to think that this novel has provided you with a different reading experience, whether or not you are familiar with catfight fiction. If it has made you aware of the apartment wrestling/rules catfighting sub-culture for the first time, welcome! I hope you might be able to use some of the information in this book to deepen and develop your interest. If you are interested in being a participant yourself, I am happy to give further advice by e-mail.

We live in an age where it is increasingly common for

women to participate in spontaneous brawls where there are no rules. I do not condone those fights for one minute. I would urge any woman who is tempted to take out her aggression on another female to follow the lead of the characters in this book. Have your fight, please, but do it in such a way that the risk of serious injury is minimised. You can do this through the medium of sport, or you can do it recreationally. But if the latter, have a small and trusted audience; use agreed rules; and follow the safety procedures which were so well documented by Barb on the Combative Women website all those years ago. And if you can, do it with love.

If you have enjoyed this book, please let me know by writing a review on Amazon. I promise to read all feedback, and it will be gratefully received. It would be even better if you could spread the word by telling your friends about this novel or posting about it on social media. As a way of thanking you, if you leave a **5* review on Amazon** and send me an e-mail to let me know, I will reply to you with some information which will give you a much better idea of Laura's appearance. It isn't a photo of her, but it's as close as you're going to get! Similarly, **if you are followed by more than 100 people on social media and you mention the novel in a post**, I would like to show my appreciation by sending you similar information about Rachel (for posts on Twitter) and Wendy (for posts on Instagram). Please use the hashtag **#evolutionsabitch** and a link to the Amazon page in your social media post, then take a screenshot of your post and e-mail it to me at my yahoo.com address. I will get back to you as soon as I can.

I have ideas for more novels in the 'authentic catfighting'

genre (my life's work will be complete when Amazon lists it as a category!), some of them based on my own experiences. If you have your own real-life experiences, which might have the potential for a novel in this genre - and don't mind sharing them - I would be delighted to hear from you.

If there is an audience, I may get around to writing a few more one day. Let me know if you would be interested in reading them.

If you would like to connect to me on social media, then look out for me under the following handles:

- Twitter: @TirnyF
- Instagram: tirnyfrancis
- Trillian: harrysears
- Freecatfights.com: Tirny Francis
- e-mail: tirnyfrancis@yahoo.com

Thank you, once again, for the time you have taken to read this book. I hope our futures will cross one day, online or in real life. And if you happen to recognise Laura, Rachel, Wendy or Mel from these pages (who said I was using their real names?) and know where they are now, say 'hello' to them from me the next time you see them.

ACKNOWLEDGEMENT

I would like to thank the content creators who have been so influential in shaping my appreciation of catfighting, both on video and recreationally. Pre-eminent is the mysterious Barb, founder of the pioneering Combative Women website. The site disappeared in 2006 but a tribute site remains and I would recommend it to anyone who is interested in reading about catfighting on the Internet and in real life at the tail-end of the twentieth century. It's a valuable relic in the modern history of catfighting. You can find it at https://sites.google.com/site/combativewomen/

I would also like to acknowledge the huge contribution to video catfight history made by the producers at Crystal Films and Danube Women Wrestling (DWW), the latter founded by the elusive, now retired Günter, known as GR in catfight circles.

Although I have not mentioned them specifically in this book, I also owe a debt of gratitude to Bob at ECNWC, another producer of astounding catfights whose name has passed into catfight legend, as well as Steve at SuiteFights, who has brought the spirit of Crystal and ECNWC into the current era with incredibly high production values.

Every fight he produces is a must-buy. Nobody does it better.

Further thanks go to the other producers whose high-quality content has fuelled this passion: in particular, Bitchfight and CatzReview in the UK; Fighting Dolls and FoxyCombat in Europe.

Thanks to Rich (Rin753) on freecatfights.com forums, whose feedback on the first draft of this book was much appreciated. The first draft of Chapter One was originally printed in its entirety on the 'Catfight, Boxing & Wrestling Stories' section of that forum (under the title of "Rachel v Laura: "You have to hurt her, or she's going to hurt you"), and I thank everyone there who provided positive feedback and encouragement, especially Kiva, whose writing I greatly admire.

More than anyone, I would like to record my thanks and admiration to the two groups of people who matter most. The first group consists of every one of those fantastic women who have ever had their catfights recorded on video for posterity. There are too many to mention but I need to single out the following as being among my favourite catfighters of all-time. From Crystal Video Magazines: Andi, Michelle, Taylor, Slick, Corrie and Mary; from DWW: Luzia, Ingrid, Barbara, Daniella, Eva and Emmanuella; from SuiteFights: Mira (oh Mira!), Jess, Lexi, Nikki and Mila Rose; from Bitchfight: Natalie, Emma, Elektra and Cassie; from ECNWC: Vira, Jenn, Gemma, Brittney, Summer and Brooke.

The second, and final group to thank, are those women who wrestle and catfight in rules-based formats in a purely recreational capacity, like Rachel, Laura, Mel and Wendy did. Whether they are doing it to test themselves, for sexual fulfilment or for the private entertainment of their significant others, I salute them. They step outside their comfort zone and risk their mental and physical well-being for reasons which people who have never done it simply do not understand. As women who are not afraid to get in touch with their own primal instincts and put them on display, I applaud them and admire them for their courage and passion.

ABOUT THE AUTHOR

Tirny Francis

Tirny Francis is a British author who has enjoyed careers in marketing and finance. Tirny has been interested in female combat of all kinds since watching the movie 'The California Dolls' (aka 'All the Marbles' in the USA) in the early nineteen-eighties. In the Internet age, Tirny has been an avid viewer of catfight videos – with a particular interest in Crystal, DWW, ECNWC and SuiteFights - and has contributed extensively to a variety of related forums and social media under different guises.

Tirny is a fan of real Japanese catfights such as the 'Japanese Babefights' series which is widely available on social media to those who know where to find it – and even claims some credit for it. Tirny has also been an active participant in recreational submission wrestling. 'Evolution's a Bitch' is Tirny's first novel.

THEMES FOR A BOOK CLUB DISCUSSION

When I embarked on this novel, I had the quaint (in retrospect) idea that it would help me to understand the appeal of recreational (aka apartment, backyard) wrestling and catfighting to spectators and participants alike. Of course, it did nothing of the sort. I finish this book with more questions than answers.

Despite the disclaimer on the inside page, this book is about a real phenomenon that involved real people. I had some involvement, all be it for a very short period of time, and was also acquainted with others who were involved in it. I cannot say whether, today, arranged rules catfights between consenting amateurs are more or less widespread than in 1997. I suspect, though, that the answer is 'much less'.

Because it is non-explanatory, I hope that the novel raises interesting questions about relationships (same sex and different sex), evolutionary behaviour, human motivation and sexual peccadilloes.

I now view *'Evolution's a Bitch'* as an exploratory novel and my hope is that it might provide the basis for a fruitful discussion of many of these issues, either in an online forum or as the subject for a book club.

The 'problematic' Title

From a commercial point of view, *'Evolution's a Bitch'* is an ineffective title. The 'B word' means that Amazon refuses to carry advertising for the book, even though it is prepared to sell it. However, *'Evolution's a Bitch'* still seems to me to be appropriate as a title, at least from a philosophical viewpoint.

Firstly, *'Evolution's a Bitch'* is intended to convey the idea that *'bitchiness'* may be a valid female survival strategy from an evolutionary perspective. Now, bitchiness in the real world rarely gets as physical as it does in this novel, but a cursory awareness of social media would seem to support the idea that bitchiness is a weapon used by many women to establish and improve their positions in a pecking order. Social hierarchies can be established through a variety of means, including physical competition, competence, access to resources and ability to network, of course. Bitchiness is not an exclusively female quality, but it has traditionally been viewed as such, rightly or wrongly. So the questions one might wish to consider which appertain to the title of this novel might include:

- What is *bitchiness?* What qualities make a bitch *'a bitch'*?
- If you had to place the characters in the novel on a spectrum of bitchiness, where would they come, and why?
- Is bitchiness an inherently female quality?
- Is the notion of 'the bitch' a stereotype or an archetype (and what is the difference?)
- What proportions of men and women attempt to

improve their positions in social hierarchies through 'bitchy' behaviour?

- How effective is bitchiness as a strategy in climbing mixed-sex, female and male hierarchies?
- Is it fair to say that men are more prone to physical aggression whilst females are more prone to psychological aggression?
- The characters in this novel manifest their aggression using physical, rather than psychological, means. Does this imply that none of them are truly 'bitches'?
- What role did physical competition play in etsablishing a pecking order among the female characters?

There is a more general message conveyed by the title: namely, that evolution itself is 'a bitch' because whether we like it or not, and whether it serves our overall happiness, we are always at the mercy of our evolutionary drives not just in matters of sex, but in all of our behaviours. So...

- If we don't admit to it being a part of our character, is there a sense in which our 'inner bitch' may be lurking in our Shadow?
- Is *'bitch'* the wrong word here? Is there a sense in which our inner **warrior** may be lurking in our Shadow, forever tethered and unleashed?
- In order to become fully-integrated individuals, how important is it that we should explore and give voice to these shadow personalities? Is rules catfighting an appropriate outlet?

And then there is the question of censorship:

- Should Amazon (or any other media) refuse to carry advertising for any product which has the word 'bitch' in it's title?

I'm not sure that 'bitch' is the best word to describe any of the female characters in this book. I hope you can discern that, from the narrator's (and my) point of view, there is something distinctly noble about all four. I want to be able to apply a word to them which respects their enthusiasm for competition and confrontation as well as their femininity.

- What should that word be?

Genre
I was stunned to discover that Amazon initially chose to categorise this novel in the BDSM sub-genre of its Erotica category, although later reconsidered. The characters in the book would certainly not have considered themselves to be participants in the BDSM scene.

- Is this book properly categorised as BDSM? If yes, what makes it so?
- Is the book 'merely' erotica, or is there more to it? If so, what?!

Evolution's a Bitch' certainly contains scenes of domination and even some cruelty. The word *'sadistic'* is mentioned four times and *'cruel'* or *'cruelty'* seven times. There are no scenes featuring bondage or masochism though.

- Is the notion of BDSM much wider than the conventional stereotype of a man in handcuffs and gimpsuit being whipped by a woman dressed in leather?
- If so, what other non-conventional forms does BDSM take?
- What explains Wendy and Rachel's need to fight each

other before they could love each other? Is it possible for us to relate to this?

- Is the ending, in which Wendy's somewhat sadistic victory over Rachel culminates in a full reconciliation between the two, fanciful or understandable?

Some, not all, viewers of professional wrestling, boxing or MMA are likely to do so because, at some level at least, it provides them with a sexual frisson.

- Is viewing such an event, or any kind of fight on video (Youtube, movies etc) symptomatic of BDSM tendencies?

Time and Place

This novel took place at a particular time and a particular place in history. The assassination of JFK in 1963 is often cited as the moment when modern America lost its innocence. I wonder if 1997 might play a similar role in the British psyche. The year began optimistically with the election of a government which promised all things to all people. In retrospect it could never have succeeded because expectations were so wildly high, but few could have predicted the level of disillusionment which persists more than a decade after the Blair government finished. There was an innocence about 1997, not just in the political optimism, but in terms of how people were adapting to arguably the most life-changing invention of the 20th century: the Internet. This is comparatively recent history, but it was also an age where social media did not exist; few people owned mobile phones; and most people who accessed the Internet did so through a slow dial-up connection.

- Could a story like the one in this book happen in the

present day?
- Are we now so spoiled for choice when it comes to having our fetishes indulged that it is just too easy and convenient for us to stay at home and download a video from clips4sale and other catfighting sites? Does this lead to us missing out on directly experiencing life's thrills?
- Has the Internet led to us 'leaving it to the experts', rather than trying it for ourselves? Do we now lead more vicarious ives thanks to the Internet?
- Do online video catfights replace the desire or need to organise rules catfights in real life?
- Did people treat each other differently online before social media entered the scene?
- For UK readers: how has Britain changed since 1997?

Themes

Hypergamy:

According to Wikipedia, hypergamy (colloquially referred to as "marrying up") is a term used in social science for the act or practice of a person marrying a spouse of higher caste or social status than themselves. The term has been used in the so-called 'manosphere' for more than a decade in relation to its role as an evolutionary strategy for women to secure 'better genes' from 'alpha males'. See the 'Rational Male' series of books (in particular Volume 1) by Rollo Tomassi, for a more detailed exposition of this concept.

In *Evolution's a Bitch*, winning a fight (whether one is male or female) always raises one's sexual attraction with others, and losing a fight always damages it.

- Are men or women more likely to be more sexually attracted to the victors of physical competition?

Laura seems to be most driven by hypergamy – to the extent that she sets up fights so that men can 'win' her as a prize. She also seems to be able to switch off her feelings for the losing fighter at will – in the manosphere, this is known as the 'war brides' dynamic. (https://therationalmale.com/2011/10/03/war-brides/). Her implied decision to abort her pregnancy by a losing fighter could be viewed as an extreme reaction to the hypergamic drive.

The narrator is apparently equally hypergamic. He is sexually attracted to the three female fighters in the moments after their respective victories, and even acknowledges that, had Mel won her catfight, he would have found himself equally powerless to resist her.

- To what extent is hypergamy and the 'war brides' theory an accurate description of female behaviour?
- To what extent are men also subject to hypergamy?
- When 'trading up', which factors are likely to be crucial for each sex? How high is physical dominance likely to rate?

Friendship

As far as we can tell, the narrator never really gets to know the other characters in any context other than catfighting and sex. His life and theirs were effectively moving at tangents to one another even though he makes a futile attempt to understand Wendy better.

- Could any of the friendships have persisted beyond the time period described in the novel? If so, which ones and why?

Safety

Catfights, as the narrator observes, are prone to get out of control. Even without this aspect, they pose a not insignificant risk of injury.

- Does this mean that recreational rules catfighting, or submission wrestling, or backyard wrestling should generally be discouraged?
- How useful are the rules laid out on Barb's page (https://sites.google.com/site/combativewomen/doing) for men or women considering recreational fighting? How could they be improved?
- We can imagine that the characters in this novel were probably aware of Barb's site and her suggested rules. How well did they stick to them, and what should they have done differently? If they didn't stick to them, what might have been the reasons? Why didn't the narrator of the novel stop Rachel's first and third fights at an earlier juncture?

Characters

- Which character would you most like to spend time with, and why? What would you like to do during your time with them?

Most of the characters have very little in the way of a backstory because the narrator knew them for a short amount of time, and because most of the time he saw them only through the lens of catfighting (and/or sex). I didn't intend the narrator to be a character worthy of sympathy but at least at the end of the novel, he recognises, and even regrets, this limitation.

- What do you imagine the backstory of the characters to be?
- How likely is it that sexual relationships pre-existed or took place between the characters in the novel that

we are told nothing about?

- We are told of one long conversation that is not related to catfighting (between Wendy and the narrator), but the narrator chooses to divulge almost nothing about it. Why do you think this is? What do you imagine was said during that conversation?

We learn in the Epilogue that Wendy is a successful professional in the current day, nearly twenty five years after the events described in *'Evolution's a Bitch'*.

- What do you think became of the other characters?

The question that confronts the narrator at the end of the epilogue is whether or not to make an effort to contact Wendy.

- What would you advise?

And merely speculating...

Wendy v. Laura: who, if either, won their catfight?

Made in the USA
Las Vegas, NV
18 July 2021

26664757R00125